A Primer in Black Holes, Mach's Principle and Gravitational Energy

Marcelo Samuel Berman

Instituto Albert Einstein
Curibita

Nova Science Publishers, Inc.
New York

NOTICE TO THE READER

The Publisher has taken reasonable care in the preparation of this book, but makes no expressed or implied warranty of any kind and assumes no responsibility for any errors or omissions. No liability is assumed for incidental or consequential damages in connection with or arising out of information contained in this book. The Publisher shall not be liable for any special, consequential, or exemplary damages resulting, in whole or in part, from the readers' use of, or reliance upon, this material.

Independent verification should be sought for any data, advice or recommendations contained in this book. In addition, no responsibility is assumed by the publisher for any injury and/or damage to persons or property arising from any methods, products, instructions, ideas or otherwise contained in this publication.

This publication is designed to provide accurate and authoritative information with regard to the subject matter covered herein. It is sold with the clear understanding that the Publisher is not engaged in rendering legal or any other professional services. If legal or any other expert assistance is required, the services of a competent person should be sought. FROM A DECLARATION OF PARTICIPANTS JOINTLY ADOPTED BY A COMMITTEE OF THE AMERICAN BAR ASSOCIATION AND A COMMITTEE OF PUBLISHERS.

LIBRARY OF CONGRESS CATALOGING-IN-PUBLICATION DATA

Berman, Marcelo Samuel.
 A primer in black holes, Mach's principle, and gravitational energy / Marcelo Samuel Berman.
   p. cm.
 Includes index.
 ISBN-13: 978-1-60021-795-1 (hardcover)
 ISBN-10: 1-60021-795-8 (hardcover)
 1. Black holes (Astronomy) 2. Mach's principle. 3. General relativity (Physics) I. Title.
QB843.B55B47 2006
523.8'875--dc22
                          2007029216

Published by Nova Science Publishers, Inc. ✦ New York

For Albert, Clarissa, Geni, Gloria, Marcos, Miguelina, Paula and Rosa.

To the victims of the Inquisition, of the Nazi regime,
and of all other forms of obscurantism.

"Aim to the Moon; even if you do not hit the bull's eye, you will direct yourself to the stars."

Lair Ribeiro, in *Feet in the Ground, Head in the Stars.* (2002)

Preface and Introduction

This textbook, designed for upper level undergraduates or beginning graduates in Theoretical Physics, eager to get acquainted with something more than a bird's eye to the theory of Black Holes, Gravitational Energy, and Mach's Principle, includes the theory of General Relativity (GRT), that could be skipped by the *conoisseurs*. Parts I and II are enlarged versions of the same parts, in Berman (2007; 2007a), which were also devoted to other aspects of GRT, mainly Cosmology. The added Sections are 2.5; 2.6; 2.7 and 3.3. A reader that would like to learn the theory without the use of tensor calculus, could very easily begin his study with Chapters 6, 7 and 8 of Part III. This part, introduces Black Holes, and some elementary calculations related to the subject. The contents of Part IV refers to the energy and angular momenta of Black Holes and the gravitomagnetic aspects (Chapter 10), and is preceded by Chapter 9, introducing variational methods. Part V is dedicated to Mach's Principle, its history and some interpretations (Chapters 11, 12 and 13). Chapter 12 introduces the concept of Machian Universes, in my own view, i.e., which are defined as those with zero-total energy. Chapter 13 studies alternative theories of gravity, in relation to Mach's Principle. Part VI (Chapter 14) closes the book with further comments and conclusions. Again, a simplified track for Parts IV and V, would be Sections 10.1, 10.2, 10.7, the entire Chapters 11-12 and Sections 13.1, 13.2 and 13.3.

Many of the studied topics, contain original papers of mine, either from Journals or from those posted in Los Alamos Archives. Our treatment of temperature and entropy, either of black holes or the Universe, is original. For instance, the loss of information paradox is dismantled: there is no paradox. Iluminating information on Black Holes may be found in the beautiful set of volumes edited by Paul V. Kreitler (Kreitler, 2006; 2006a; 2006b).

Because I belong to minorities (Jews and Argentines), I faced discrimination and injustice, during the Brazilian military and dictatorial regime, and even later. Nevertheless, I still believe that Science is a tool against obscurantism. It was this confidence in Science, that led me forward, towards the pursuit of knowledge.

I thank the many colleagues and friends who collaborated towards the elaboration of this book, too many to be cited one by one; I can not omit Antonio F. da F. Teixeira, Nelson Suga, M.M. Som, Fernando de Mello Gomide, Rubens de Melo Marinho Jr, Homero Santiago Maciel, and Tobias Federico. A warm and enthusiastic incentive, has been granted to me by the most important Latin American expert in the foundations of Physics and Mathematical logic, Newton da Costa, who was also my high school teacher. I also owe a lot of gratitude to Henrique Fleming.

The good typing, is due to Marcelo Fermann Guimarães, who did not spare his efforts in order to bring a careful manuscript. Neither he (who does not even understand Physics),

Part I

MATHEMATICAL PRELIMINARIES

If we compare both systems of coordinates we will find between S and S', relations of the type:

$$x'^i = F^i(x^j),$$ (1.2.1)

where $\mid i = 1, ... , N$

$\mid j = 1, ... , N$
$\mid F^i$ = one to one function, continuous with continuous derivatives of any order.

Taking the differential of relation (1.2.1) we obtain by the rules of differential calculus:

$$dx'^i = \sum_{j=1}^{N} \frac{\partial x'^i}{\partial x^j} dx^j.$$ (1.2.2)

From now on, we shall adhere to Einstein's sum convention, under which when one index is repeated twice in the same term of an equation, a sum over all values of that index is assumed. For example, we shall re-write (1.2.2) as:

$$dx'^i = \frac{\partial x'^i}{\partial x^j} dx^j.$$ (1.2.3)

Repeated indices are called in English language as "dummies".

We now introduce the symbol δ^i_j, called Kronecker's delta. It is defined by the following relations:

$$\delta^i_j = 1 \quad \text{if} \quad i = j,$$

$$\delta^i_j = 0 \quad \text{if} \quad i \neq j.$$

A very useful mathematical relation is the following one:

$$\frac{\partial x^i}{\partial x^j} = \delta^i_j \quad .$$ (1.2.4)

The above relation expresses that different coordinates are independent of one another. Applying a well known rule from Calculus, we can write from (1.2.4) that:

$$\frac{\partial x^i}{\partial x'^j} \frac{\partial x'^j}{\partial x^k} = \delta^i_k \quad .$$ (1.2.5)

Contravariant Vectors

Relation (1.2.3) defines the transformation law for the components of the displacement vector (dx^i) between two infinitesimally nearby points. Each set of N quantities V^i which transform likewise, is called the set of components of a contravariant vector, so that the prototype vector V'^i in system S' is related to V^j in S by

$$V'^i = \frac{\partial x'^i}{\partial x^j} V^j \quad .$$ (1.2.6)

Contravariant Tensors of 2ND Rank

Let T^{ij} be a set of N^2 quantities which transform according to the law

$$T'^{ij} = \frac{\partial x'^i}{\partial x^k} \frac{\partial x'^j}{\partial x^l} T^{kl} \quad . \tag{1.2.7}$$

The above set T^{ij} is said to represent a contravariant tensor of 2nd rank. By the same token, higher order tensors could be defined. A closed analysis by the reader should suffice to check that by multiplying two contravariant vectors U^i and V^j , we obtain a 2nd rank contravariant tensor, and so on. However not always one could decompose a given tensor of superior order into the product of vectors. The reader may check also that by the given definitions, a contravariant vector is a tensor of first rank. The rank zero tensor is called an invariant; let ϕ and ϕ' represent an invariant in S and S' coordinate systems: obviously,

$$\phi = \phi' \quad . \tag{1.2.8}$$

Covariant Vectors

Suppose that $\phi = \phi (x^i)$, is an invariant in each point of space, but a function of the coordinates x^i. From Calculus comes the relation

$$\frac{\partial \phi}{\partial x'^i} = \frac{\partial \phi}{\partial x^j} \frac{\partial x^j}{\partial x'^i} \quad . \tag{1.2.9}$$

The reader should not have any trouble for identifying the "vector" $\frac{\partial \phi}{\partial x^j}$ as the gradient of ϕ . Each set of quantities V_i that transforms according to the gradient, i.e., according to (1.2.9), so that:

$$V'_j = \frac{\partial x^i}{\partial x'^j} V_i \quad , \tag{1.2.10}$$

is called the set of components of a "covariant" vector, also called covector. As is clear in our notation, we adopt the convention of representing superior indices as a sign of contravariancy, while down indices represent covariance.

Covariant Tensors of 2nd Rank

A set of quantities T_{ij} is called the set of components of a 2nd rank covariant tensor if when transformed to the system S' we obtain the set T'_{ij} defined as:

$$T'_{ij} = \frac{\partial x^k}{\partial x'^i} \frac{\partial x^l}{\partial x'^j} T_{kl} \quad . \tag{1.2.11}$$

Covariant tensors of higher order are defined analogously. The reader can check that the covariant tensor of 1st rank is a covector. The invariant is a covariant tensor of zero rank. In other words, the invariant is both covariant and contravariant. Like in the contravariant tensor case, the product of a covariant vector with components V_i with another covariant vector U_j yields a covariant tensor of 2nd rank but it is useful to remember that not all covariant tensors of 2nd rank can be decomposed into the product of two covariant vectors.

Demonstration:

Let the given equation be valid in system S:

$$A^i_j = B^i_j \ .$$

Transforming into the coordinate system S' it is obvious that both sides transform in the same way, verbi gratia, like a mixed tensor of 2nd rank (with other type of tensors the reasoning would not be any different), so that:

$$A'^i_j = B'^i_j \ .$$

Simply stated, a tensor equation is valid in any system of coordinates. The mathematical reason behind this theorem is that tensor transformations are linear and homogeneous. Immediately one can conclude that any equation of the type $C^i_j = 0$ implies that

$$C'^i_j = 0 \ , \quad \text{provided that we are dealing with a tensor.}$$

(Remember that not all matrices of 2nd rank transform like tensors). In the above example if you write

$$C^i_j = A^i_j - B^i_j = 0 \ , \quad \text{it is clear that} \quad A'^i_j = B'^i_j \ .$$

Exterior Product

The exterior product of two tensors was introduced earlier in the particular case when we commented that the product $V^j U_i$ of two vectors makes a 2nd rank tensor. A new tensor is always obtained which has a rank given by the sum of the ranks of the involved tensors in the exterior product, by the multiplication of the components of two or more tensors. As no summing is implicit in exterior product, care must be taken in order to represent each multiplying factor with different literal indices without repetition. For instance, suppose that we are given two tensors, say, A^r_{st} and B^{ik}_j. We multiply exteriorly to obtain a new tensor: C^{rik}_{stj} .

The value of each component of the new tensor will be given by:

$$C^{rik}_{stj} = A^r_{st} B^{ik}_j \ .$$

Contraction

Let a given mixed tensor be contracted which means that we write one index of covariant type equal to a given contravariant index: we claim that the resultant tensor has a rank two units less than the original rank. In other words, the contracted tensor has a rank which results from computing the left untouched indices.

Demonstration: consider the tensor A^i_{jkl}. By definition the law of transformation is:

$$A'^i_{jkl} = \frac{\partial x'^i}{\partial x^r} \frac{\partial x^s}{\partial x'^j} \frac{\partial x^t}{\partial x'^k} \frac{\partial x^p}{\partial x'^l} A^r_{stp} \ .$$

On contracting, i.e., writing $i = j$ we are left with:

$$A'^i_{ikl} = \left(\frac{\partial x'^i}{\partial x^r} \frac{\partial x^s}{\partial x'^i} \right) \frac{\partial x^t}{\partial x'^k} \frac{\partial x^p}{\partial x'^l} A^r_{stp} = \frac{\partial x^t}{\partial x'^k} \frac{\partial x^p}{\partial x'^l} A^r_{rtp} \ , \quad \text{where we made use of (1.2.5).}$$

Q.O.D.

Interior Product

We define the interior product of two tensors by the exterior product followed by a contraction.

Tests of Tensor Character

Given a certain set of quantities, we would like to test the set in order to check whether we are in face of a tensor. The direct test is to check how the given set of quantities behaves under a coordinate transformation, say, from S to S'. Nevertheless, sometimes it is more useful to apply the so called Quotient Theorem which allows an indirect test: "if the interior product of the set "X" with an arbitrary tensor is a tensor, then X is a tensor". We leave it to the reader to demonstrate this theorem for a particular tensor like a 2nd rank contravariant. In other cases, the proof runs equally well.

1.4. Final Observations

1) **Transitivity-** Besides linearity and homogeneity the transformation property of tensors is endowed with transitivity. By transitivity we mean the following: if in a transformation from the coordinate system S to S' a given set X transforms according to the tensor definition, and the same happens from coordinate system S' to a third system S'' we are sure that the tensor character will be assured again. If this does not happen, the tensor definition would not be transitive. Let us demonstrate it for a 2nd rank contravariant tensor T^{ij} : the hypotheses are:

$$T'^{ij} = \frac{\partial x'^i}{\partial x^k} \frac{\partial x'^j}{\partial x^l} T^{kl} \ . \tag{1.4.1}$$

and,

$$T''^s = \frac{\partial x''^r}{\partial x'^i} \frac{\partial x''^s}{\partial x'^j} T'^{ij} \ . \tag{1.4.2}$$

The thesis is:

$$T'' = \frac{\partial x''^r}{\partial x^k} \frac{\partial x''^s}{\partial x^l} T^{kl} \ . \tag{1.4.3}$$

We demonstrate easily that substituting (1.4.2) into (1.4.1), and by applying twice the relation (1.2.5) we obtain (1.4.3).

2) **Tensorial Field**: The tensors defined in this Chapter refer to points in an amorphous space (Synge and Schild (1969)), what means that in this space there is no definition of distance between neighborhood points (the metric of the space is not necessarily defined yet). Everything which is valid for isolated points in space, may be valid for a continuum, in which case we define a tensor field.

3) **Symmetry and Anti-symmetry**: A tensor of any order is said symmetric relative to a pair of indices of the same type, if the numerical value is not altered by an interchanged of those indices.

Example: if $T^{rsl}_{pq} = T^{srl}_{pq}$ then the tensor is symmetric relative to the first two contravariant indices.

We define an anti-symmetric tensor, relative to a pair of indices of the same type, if upon exchange of those indices, the components change the algebraic sign.

Example: suppose $T^{rsl}_{pq} = -T^{rsl}_{qp}$; then the tensor is anti-symmetric relative to the two covariant indices.

Anti-symmetric tensors are also called skew-symmetric tensors.

The reader may easily demonstrate that symmetry or anti-symmetry properties are conserved in a transformation of coordinates, for a tensor. This does not imply that an equality of the type:

$$T^{rsl}_{pq} = T^{psl}_{rq} \quad ,$$

will be kept under a transformation of coordinates. As an exercise the reader should show that the above is true.

In the next chapter use will be made of the following Theorem: "let $\Phi = g_{ij}X^i X^j$ be an invariant while X^i and X^j are arbitrary contravariant vectors and g_{ij} is a set of symmetric quantities in all system of coordinates. Then, g_{ij} stands for a 2nd rank covariant tensor".

4) **Riemannian Spaces:** For the reader versed in differential geometry we want to advance the idea that we shall need to particularize the otherwise amorphous space of this Chapter into a metric Riemannian space which is torsionless, where the affinities are the Christoffel symbols and there is a metric tensor of 2nd rank which is symmetric. The whole story is left for next Chapter.

References for Chapter 1

At this stage, the reader may benefit from consulting more advanced treatises like Weinberg (1972), Adler, Bazin and Schiffer (1975) or MTW (1973). These references are basic and highly recommended reading.

Chapter 2

Tensors in Riemann Spaces

2.1. Metric

In Euclidean Geometry, it is true that the distance between infinitesimally nearby points is an invariant. Choosing Cartesian orthogonal coordinates, we shall have:

$$ds^2 = dx^i dx^i \quad = \quad \text{invariant,} \qquad (2.1.1)$$

where a summation from 1 to 3 is implied by the repeated index i.

In curvilinear coordinates, ds^2, called in general the metric form or the fundamental space form or the square of the line element, is given by an expression of the type:

$$ds^2 = g_{ij} dx^i dx^j \quad . \qquad (2.1.2)$$

For instance, in spherical coordinates, we shall have:

$$g_{11} = 1,$$

$$g_{22} = r^2 \ , \qquad (2.1.3)$$

$$g_{33} = r^2 sen^2\theta \ ,$$

$$g_{ij} = 0 \ , \text{ for } i \neq j \ .$$

The 2nd rank covariant tensor, g_{ij}, is called covariant metric tensor or the fundamental space tensor. Notice that we may consider, a priori, the tensor g_{ij} to be symmetric, having in mind the commutativity of the product $dx^i dx^j$, and the subsequent verification that in expressions (2.1.2), only occur sums of the type

$$(g_{ij} + g_{ji}) \ .$$

Notice also that the proof that g_{ij} is a 2nd rank covariant tensor is obtainable from last Chapter theorem from Section 1.4 where we take

$$\Phi = ds^2 \ ,$$

$$X^i = dx^i \ .$$

We say that the metric is indefinite whenever it may assume positive, negative or null numerical values. In the case of General Relativity Theory, as well as in the particular case where there is no gravitational field (Special Relativity) this can indeed happen. Recall Minkowski's spacetime metric:

$$ds^2 = - \left[dx^2 + dy^2 + dz^2\right] + c^2 dt^2, \qquad (2.1.4)$$

where c stands for the speed of light in vacuum for an inertial observer, and (x, y, z) are the space coordinates while t is the temporal coordinate. It is evident that the metric may be positive, negative or null. If $ds^2 = 0$, we say that the metric defines a null displacement, characteristic of light rays.

Riemann spaces are spaces that admit a metric of the type (2.1.2) where the covariant metric tensor is symmetric ($g_{ij} = g_{ji}$) .

Contravariant Metric Tensor

On considering g_{ij} like a square matrix, we can define a new tensor g^{ij} from the matrix above by the relation:

$$g^{ij} = \frac{\Delta^{ij}}{g} \ , \qquad (2.1.4)$$

where

$\Delta^{ij} =$ cofactor matrix for g_{ij}
$g =$ determinant of g_{ij} .

Taken that g_{ij} is symmetric, and from the definition of a matrix inverse, we find that:

$$g_{ij} g^{jk} = \delta_i^k \ . \qquad (2.1.5)$$

The tensor g^{jk} is sometimes called the conjugate tensor of g_{jk} .

In Riemannian spaces, distinct from amorphous spaces, there is no distinction among the covariant tensors, the contravariants or the mixed, when they refer to the same geometric entity. In fact, given any tensor T_k^{ij} we associate to it the tensor

$$S^{ijk} = g^{lk} T_l^{ij} \ . \qquad (2.1.6)$$

Now, let us associate to the tensor S^{ijk} a new tensor:

$$R_k^{ij} = g_{lk} S^{ijl} \ . \qquad (2.1.7)$$

A close examination reveals that

$$R_k^{ij} \equiv T_k^{ij} \quad . \tag{2.1.8}$$

We conclude, therefore, that the metric tensors work as operators that lower down an index or raise up an index. When we apply this operator once there is no new tensor being created; however we have another representation of the same geometrical entity. In order to ensure proper mathematical consistency we shall use the same letter to represent the same entity with some raised or lowered indices, for example T_k^{ij} and T^{ijk}.

From relation (2.1.5) it is evident that Kronecker's delta is the mixed form of the metric tensor.

2.2. Christoffel Symbols

We define now Christoffel symbols of the 1st and 2nd kind, respectively:

$$\Gamma_{ijk} = \frac{1}{2} \left(\frac{\partial g_{ik}}{\partial x^j} + \frac{\partial g_{kj}}{\partial x^i} - \frac{\partial g_{ij}}{\partial x^k} \right) \quad , \tag{2.2.1}$$

$$\Gamma_{jk}^i = g^{il} \Gamma_{jkl} \quad . \tag{2.2.2}$$

Notwithstanding the fact that the symbols Γ_{ijk} and Γ_{jk}^i contain indices, they do not represent tensors as we shall show below.

We shall now show that in a change of coordinates from system S to system S' the Christoffel symbol of the 1st kind Γ_{ijk} transforms itself into Γ'_{ijk} given by the following expression:

$$\Gamma'_{ijk} = \Gamma_{lmn} \frac{\partial x^l}{\partial x'^i} \frac{\partial x^m}{\partial x'^j} \frac{\partial x^n}{\partial x'^k} + g_{lm} \frac{\partial x^l}{\partial x'^k} \frac{\partial^2 x^m}{\partial x'^i \partial x'^j} \quad . \tag{2.2.3}$$

Before we derive this relation, we must point out that it is not in the form of a tensor transformation: the right hand side of the above formula contains two terms summed, the 1st of which if if stood alone, would warrant the tensorial nature of the Christoffel symbol of the 1st kind and consequently, of the 2nd kind too.

Demonstration:

From the definition property of a covariant 2nd rank tensor applied to the metric tensor:

$$g'_{jk} = \frac{\partial x^l}{\partial x'^j} \frac{\partial x^m}{\partial x'^k} g_{lm} \quad . \tag{2.2.4}$$

Applying the partial derivative symbol relative to x'^n to both sides of the above equation, we find by the usual Differential Calculus rules:

Its very easy to show that:

$$V^i_{;j;k} - V^i_{;k;j} = -R^i_{lkj}V^l \qquad (2.4.1)$$

and

$$V_{i;j;k} - V_{i;k;j} = R^l_{ijk}V_l \qquad (2.4.2)$$

where

$$R^l_{ijk} \equiv \frac{\partial \Gamma^l_{ik}}{\partial x^j} - \frac{\partial \Gamma^l_{ji}}{\partial x^k} + \Gamma^m_{ik}\Gamma^l_{jm} - \Gamma^m_{ij}\Gamma^l_{km} . \qquad (2.4.3)$$

The proof of the above is direct: one has only to apply relations (2.3.6) and (2.3.7), combined with (2.3.4) and (2.3.5).

The fourth rank tensor R^i_{jkl} is the famous curvature tensor or Riemann-Christoffel tensor.

Ricci Tensor

By definition, the Ricci Tensor R_{ij} is given by:

$$R_{ij} = R^l_{ilj} \quad . \qquad (2.4.4)$$

Ricci Scalar Curvature

By definition, the Ricci Scalar Curvature R is given by:

$$R \equiv R^i_i \equiv g^{ij}R_{ij} \quad . \qquad (2.4.5)$$

Einstein's Tensor

By definition, Einstein's Tensor G_{ij} is given by:

$$G_{ij} = R_{ij} - \tfrac{1}{2}g_{ij}R \quad . \qquad (2.4.6)$$

Geodesic Coordinate System

A coordinate system is called geodesic, if in a considered point of spacetime, all the components of the Christoffel symbols are null.

Theorem:
"It is always possible, in a given point in spacetime, to build a geodesic coordinate system".

We now demonstrate this theorem:

Consider a coordinate system S in which, for a given spacetime point the gammas are different from zero: $\Gamma^i_{jk} \neq 0$.

We now go to another system of coordinates S' which has the following property:

$$x'^i = x^i - x^i_0 + \tfrac{1}{2} \left(\Gamma^i_{jk}\right)_0 \left[x^j - x^j_0\right]\left[x^k - x^k_0\right] .$$ (2.4.7)

The index zero indicates the values of the quantities in the point where the geodesic coordinate system is defined.

We now obtain the null $\left(\Gamma'_{ijk}\right)_0$ by means of relation (2.2.6) if we introduce the following results obtained from (2.4.7):

$$\left(\tfrac{\partial x'^i}{\partial x^j}\right)_0 = \delta^i_j$$

$$\left(\tfrac{\partial x^i}{\partial x'^j}\right)_0 = \delta^i_j$$

$$\left(\tfrac{\partial^2 x^i}{\partial x'^j \partial x'^k}\right)_0 = \left(-\Gamma^i_{jk}\right)_0 .$$

Q.E.D.

Theorem:
"In a geodesic system, the partial derivatives of the metric tensor are all null".

Demonstration

We know that the covariant derivatives of the metric tensor are null; however in a geodesic system of coordinates the covariant derivative of the metric tensor equals the partial derivative, so these are also null.

Bianchi Identity

In a geodesic system of coordinates, all the Christoffel symbols are null, but not necessarily the derivatives are null too. In such case we may write:

$$R^i_{jkl;m} = \frac{\partial^2 \Gamma^i_{jl}}{\partial x^m \partial x^k} - \frac{\partial^2 \Gamma^i_{jk}}{\partial x^m \partial x^l} .$$ (2.4.8)

On applying the above equation three times, we obtain:

$$R^i_{jkl;m} + R^i_{jlm;k} + R^i_{jmk;l} = 0 .$$ (2.4.9)

This is a tensorial equation valid for a geodesic coordinate system. However, according to the Fundamental Theorem of Tensor Calculus, derived in Chapter 1, it must be valid in any system: it is called Bianchi Identity.

$$\frac{\partial g}{\partial x^\mu} = g g^{\alpha\beta} g_{\alpha\beta,\mu}.$$ (2.5.8)

We may now find a useful expression for $\Gamma^\beta_{\alpha\beta}$, to wit,

$$\Gamma^\beta_{\alpha\beta} = g^{\lambda\beta}\Gamma_{\lambda\alpha\beta} = \tfrac{1}{2}g^{\lambda\beta}\left(g_{\lambda\alpha,\beta} + g_{\lambda\beta,\alpha} - g_{\alpha\beta,\lambda}\right) = \tfrac{1}{2}g_{\lambda\beta,\alpha}g^{\lambda\beta} .$$ (2.5.9)

This may also be written as,

$$\Gamma^\beta_{\alpha\beta} = \tfrac{1}{2}g^{-1}g_{,\alpha} = \tfrac{1}{2}\left(\log g\right)_{,\alpha} .$$ (2.5.10)

We may, on the other hand, calculate the following expression:

$$2\Gamma^\mu_{\alpha\mu} = g^{-1}g_{,\alpha} = 2\left(\sqrt{-g}\right)^{-1}\left(\sqrt{-g}\right)_{,\alpha} = n\left[\sqrt{-g}\right]^{-1/n}\left\{\left[\sqrt{-g}\right]^{1/n}\right\}_{,\alpha} = n\left(g^{1/n}\right)_{,\alpha} .$$ (2.5.11)

Once more, we have further,

$$\Gamma^\mu_{\alpha\mu}\sqrt{-g} = \left[\sqrt{-g}\right]_{,\alpha} = \tfrac{1}{2}\sqrt{-g}\,g^{\lambda\mu}g_{\lambda\mu,\alpha}.$$ (2.5.12)

It will not be applied later, but we must mention that more general tensor densities can be defined; for instance, $g = \det g_{\mu\nu}$ is in fact called a tensor density of weight (-2), because this is the power of J that appears in the transformation relation,

$$g' = J^{-2}g.$$ (2.5.13)

We remark that the product of a tensor density of weight (-1), with the volume element d^4x , transforms as a real tensor.

2.6. Geodesics

The equations of free motion in GRT, mean the equations of motion in the presence of gravitational fields; it is called free motion, because the gravitational field is considered as a cause for the curving of spacetime, and not the existence of an external force. In the absence of gravitation, as it is well known, a particle would traverse on straight lines, which means that the acceleration is null, i.e.,

$$\frac{d^2x^i}{dt^2} = 0 .$$ (2.6.1)

The above equation stems from Newtonian Mechanics.

In Special Relativity, we define the relativistic force by the equation,

$$f^\alpha = m\frac{d^2x^\alpha}{d\tau^2} ,$$ (2.6.2)

where τ stands for proper time. In the zero-force case, we are left with:

$$\frac{d^2x^\alpha}{d\tau^2} = 0 \,, \tag{2.6.3}$$

The relation between proper time and coordinate time, is given by:

$$d\tau^2 = \frac{ds^2}{c^2} = dt^2 - \frac{v^2}{c^2}\left(d\,\vec{r}\right)^2 = dt^2 - \frac{1}{c^2}\left(dx^2 + dy^2 + dz^2\right) \,. \tag{2.6.4}$$

In other words, we may write the Special relativistic equation of zero-acceleration as:

$$\frac{d^2x^\alpha}{ds^2} = 0 \,. \tag{2.6.5}$$

As the passage to Riemannian geometry, i.e., curved spacetime, implies in the transformation of common derivatives into covariant ones, we may write the corresponding equations, in GRT, of (2.6.5), as:

$$\frac{D^2x^\alpha}{Ds^2} = 0 \,, \tag{2.6.6}$$

or, using the definition of covariant derivatives,

$$\frac{d^2x^\alpha}{ds^2} + \Gamma^\alpha_{\mu\nu}\frac{dx^\mu}{ds}\frac{dx^\nu}{ds} = 0 \,. \tag{2.6.7}$$

We know that, in flat spacetime, a straight line between two points, is an extrema of the arc length, between the same two points; it is represented by equations (2.6.3). In fact, they are the geodesics of flat spacetime. By analogy, equations (2.6.7) define the condition for arc length extrema between two points in Riemann geometry. It is easy to understand, that the Γ's are null in Cartesian coordinates; they are not null, even in flat spacetime, when we employ curvilinear coordinates. In any case, we are left with extrema equations for the arc length s .

2.7. Geodesic Deviation

From the analysis of neighboring geodesics, we may know whether we are in face of a flat spacetime, or a curved one. As the curved one, represents a gravitational field, we can calculate the geodesic deviation equation, which measures how the displacement vector, who measures the "distance" between any two neighboring geodesics, depends on the curvature of spacetime, represented by the Riemann-Christoffel tensor. If there is a non-linear change in such displacement, we can say that we are in face of a gravitational field.

We now attach rigorous meaning to the above qualitative arguments.

Consider a family o geodesics, $x^\alpha(s,p)$, where s is the arc length along each one geodesic curve, and p is a label for each individual geodesic curve. In 3-D space, all the considered geodesics should be on a surface. If the geodesic are straight neighboring lines, in a flat surface, but employing curvilinear coordinates (non-Cartesian), we could measure the displacement between each two neighboring geodesics, having the same s - value . If this displacement is a linear function of s , we are in face of a flat surface. In 4-D spacetime, a flat 3-D space would mean that there is no gravitational field.

Chapter 3

Complements of Tensor Calculus (Optional Study)

3.1. Orthogonal Transformations and Cartesian Tensors

Two coordinate systems S and S' relate themselves by means of an orthogonal transformation, if it can be expressed like:

$$x'^i = a_{ij}x^j + b^i , \qquad (3.1.1)$$

where a_{ij} and b^i are constants.

In a orthogonal transformation, the distance between two points, x_0^i and x^i is defined by its square:

$$s'^2 = (x'^i - x_0'^i)(x'^i - x_0'^i),$$

which is an invariant, i.e.:

$$s'^2 = s^2 . \qquad (3.1.2)$$

We define:

$$\Delta x^i = x^i - x_0^i ,$$

and we verify that (3.1.1) can be written like:

$$\Delta x'^i = a_{ij}\Delta x^j , \qquad (3.1.3)$$

or in matrix form:

$$\Delta x' = A\Delta x . \qquad (3.1.4)$$

If we call the transpose of $\Delta x'$, as $(\Delta x')^T$, we may write:

$$(\Delta x')^T(\Delta x') = (\Delta x)^T(\Delta x) = s^2 . \qquad (3.1.5)$$

It must be remembered, however, that the covariant derivative along a curve may be the only one that we may calculate.

We define now the **parallel transport** of a tensor along a given curve, as the law which makes that its covariant derivative along the curve be zero. For instance, consider a contravariant vector A^i. The law of its parallel transport is given by:

$$dA^i = -\Gamma^i_{jk}A^j dx^k .$$ (3.2.4)

In order to understand the physical meaning of this law, consider parallel transport in a geodesic system of coordinates:

$$dA^i = 0 .$$

Obviously its covariant derivative is also null:

$$\frac{DA^i}{Ds} = 0 .$$

(in this coordinate system)

Thus, the vector does not change its size or direction. As the tensor properties are independent of the particular coordinate system to be employed, what we have said, is valid for the general case: the transported vector "does not change its size or direction". By means of parallel transport, we may compare two tensors located at different points of spacetime.

We may now interpret anew the equations of geodesics. As we saw in Chapter 3, it is given by:

$$\frac{d^2 x^i}{ds^2} + \Gamma^i_{jk}\frac{dx^j}{ds}\frac{dx^k}{ds} = 0 .$$

We rewrite the above as:

$$\frac{D}{Ds}\left(\frac{dx^i}{ds}\right) = 0 .$$ (3.2.5)

Or:

$$\frac{D}{Ds}t^i = 0 ,$$ (3.2.6)

where $t^i = \frac{dx^i}{ds}$ is the vector tangent to the curve $x^i = x^i(s)$ by definition.

We are now in condition to say that the geodesics equation warrants that the tangent vector to geodesic curve is parallel-to-itself transported along the curve.

3.3.   Tetrads

The importance of this Section, lies not only on the pure geometric notions that we shall advance, but on its consequences, because Einstein's field equations may be subjected to a tetrad formalism. In this book, we shall not follow this line of development, for we only mention collaterally the field equations. The reader may follow most of the contents of Parts III, IV and V, which are the core of this book, without worrying with these details. Nevertheless, we have written this Section, in order to lay the ground for future developments, to be studied by the reader in further endeavors, for instance, through Newman-Penrose formalism (Chandrasekhar, 1983).

Consider a given point of space. We attach a reference frame, at that point, which is defined by four linearly independent vectors, called tetrads, $h_\alpha^{(\beta)}$. In a four-dimensional space, the index (β) identifies one among the four vectors of the tetrad. Each vector has four components, i.e., for each value of (β) , identifying each vector in the tetrad, we have vector components identified by the α - value. In other words, the components of one vector in the tetrad, defined by a fixed β , are given by: $h_0^{(\beta)}$, $h_1^{(\beta)}$, $h_2^{(\beta)}$, $h_3^{(\beta)}$. The number (β) is called the tetrad index. The number α , as it is clear, identifies the component of each tetrad member.

Nothing can deter us from defining, in analogy to the above representation, new components for lower tetrad indices, to wit,

$$h_{(\beta)\alpha} = g_{(\beta)(\gamma)}h_\alpha^{(\gamma)}. \tag{3.3.1}$$

This defines a symmetric matrix,

$$g^{(\beta)(\gamma)} = h_\alpha^{(\beta)}h_\delta^{(\gamma)}g^{\alpha\delta} . \tag{3.3.2}$$

Though this is not a game, we may "play" with the formalism, finding a matrix $g_{(\beta)(\gamma)}$ that lowers the tetrad indices, like,

$$g_{(\beta)(\gamma)}g^{(\gamma)(\varepsilon)} = \delta_{(\beta)}^{(\varepsilon)} \equiv g_{(\beta)}^{(\varepsilon)}, \tag{3.3.3}$$

and so on. For instance, the components of the covariant metric tensor, are given by,

$$g_{\alpha\delta} = g_{(\beta)(\gamma)}h_\alpha^{(\beta)}h_\delta^{(\gamma)} . \tag{3.3.4}$$

Now we go a step further, and define tetrad components of tensors. Consider a general case for a tensor with contravariant indices $\alpha , \beta , ...$ and covariant indices $\mu , \nu , ...$ The tetrad components for a general tensor $T_{\mu\nu...}^{\alpha\beta...}$ are given by:

$$T_{(\mu)(\nu)...}^{(\alpha)(\beta)...} = T_{nm...}^{rs...}h_r^{(\alpha)}h_s^{(\beta)}h_{(\mu)}^n h_{(\nu)}^m \cdots . \tag{3.3.5}$$

Instead of representing the tetrad tensor components in terms of the tensor components and the tetrad vectors, we may write the reversed expression, and call this, the Lie derivative of tensor $T(x)$ in the direction of vector $a^i(x)$, at point Q.

Alternatively, because points P and Q coincide in the limit, we could have defined the same Lie derivative as above by means of:

$$L_{a^i} T(x) = \lim_{\varepsilon \to 0} \left[\frac{T(x) - T'(x)}{\varepsilon} \right] . \qquad (3.5.4)$$

The two definitions are equivalent; the Lie derivative measure the variation of a tensor when the observer moves from one point to a neighboring point in a given direction, retaining its coordinate system.

Example 1: Calculate $L_a \phi(x)$, where ϕ is an invariant,

Consider that:

$$\phi(x) = \phi'(x'). \qquad (3.5.5)$$

Let us apply the first definition: on point Q we have:

$$T(x') = \phi(x') = \phi(x + \varepsilon a) = \phi(x) + \varepsilon a^i \frac{\partial \phi}{\partial x^i} ,$$

and,

$$T'(x') = \phi'(x') = \phi(x) .$$

Then,

$$L_a \phi(x) = \lim_{\varepsilon \to 0} \left[\phi(x) + \varepsilon a^i \frac{\partial \phi}{\partial x^i} - \phi(x) \right] \varepsilon^{-1} = a^i \frac{\partial \phi}{\partial x^i} . \qquad (3.5.6)$$

Example 2: Calculate $L_a V^i(x)$, i.e., obtain the Lie derivative of a contravariant vector.

Let us apply the second definition:

$$V'^j(x') = V'^j(x^i + \varepsilon a^i) = V'^j(x) + \varepsilon a^i \frac{\partial V'^j}{\partial x^i} \cong V'^j + \varepsilon a^i \frac{\partial V^j}{\partial x^i} , \qquad (3.5.7)$$

where in the last term, we neglected second order infinitessimal ($\varepsilon^2 \cong 0$). From the definition of a contravariant transformation,

$$V'^j(x') = V^k(x) \frac{\partial x'^j}{\partial x^k} . \qquad (3.5.8)$$

On the other hand,

$$\frac{\partial x'^j}{\partial x^k} = \frac{\partial}{\partial x^k} \left[x^j + \varepsilon a^j \right] = \delta^j_k + \varepsilon \frac{\partial a^j}{\partial x^k} . \qquad (3.5.9)$$

From the last two relations, we obtain:

$$V'^j(x') = V^k \delta_k^j + \varepsilon V^k \frac{\partial a^j}{\partial x^k} = V^j + \varepsilon V^k \frac{\partial a^j}{\partial x^k} . \tag{3.5.10}$$

From (3.5.7) and (3.5.10), we find:

$$V'^j + \varepsilon a^i \frac{\partial V^j}{\partial x^i} = V^j + \varepsilon V^k \frac{\partial a^j}{\partial x^k} .$$

Then,

$$L_a V^i(x) = \lim_{\varepsilon \to 0} \left[\varepsilon \left(a^i \frac{\partial V^j}{\partial x^i} - V^k \frac{\partial a^j}{\partial x^k} \right) \right] \varepsilon^{-1} = a^i \frac{\partial V^j}{\partial x^i} - V^i \frac{\partial a^j}{\partial x^i} . \tag{3.5.11}$$

Analogously, we could find the Lie derivatives of any other kind of tensor.

Important result: in a Riemann space, the reader might check that an alternative but equivalent expression for relation (3.5.11) could be obtained by substituting partial derivatives by covariant derivatives; this conclusion is general and allows us to infer that the Lie derivative of a tensor, in Riemann space, is also a tensor.

Further results.

1st) The reader may check that:

$$L_a V_n = V_{n;i} a^i + V_i a_{;n}^i .$$

$$L_a g_{mn} = a_{m;n} + a_{n;m}, \tag{3.5.12}$$

where g_{mn} is the metric tensor component.

2nd) it obeys the usual rules for the derivative of sums and products.

3rd) it commutes with the contraction.

4th) it commutes with partial derivatives.

3.6. Isometries

The study of the symmetries in Riemann space, begins with the calculation of the variation of the metric tensor in given directions of space.

Definition: Isometric mapping is an infinitesimal coordinate transformation under which the Lie derivative of the metric tensor becomes null:

$$L_a g_{ij}(x) = 0 . \tag{3.6.1}$$

On remembering relation (3.5.12), we find then:

$$a_{i;j} + a_{j;i} = 0 \ .$$

(3.6.2)

This is the famous Killing equation, whose solutions, if they exist, allow the isometric mapping. The solutions $a_i(x)$ are the Killing vectors, and if they exist, we say that the space has intrinsic symmetries.

Example: Find the intrinsic symmetries of the Euclidean plane, i.e., solve Killing's equations for the Euclidean plane.

Solution:

In Cartesian coordinates,

$$ds^2 = dx^2 + dy^2$$

$$\therefore g_{AB} = \delta_{AB} \quad \text{where} \quad A, B = 1, 2 \ .$$

Killing equation reduces to:

$$\frac{\partial a^1}{\partial x} = \frac{\partial a^2}{\partial y} = 0 \ .$$

(3.5.3)

and,

$$\frac{\partial a^1}{\partial y} + \frac{\partial a^2}{\partial x} = 0 \ .$$

(3.5.4)

By integration of the first equation (3.5.3) we find:

$$a^1 = Y(y) \ .$$

and,

$$a^2 = X(x) \ .$$

On taking to the second equation (3.5.4) the above results become:

$$\frac{dY(y)}{dy} + \frac{dX(x)}{dx} = 0 \ .$$

This last equation can be solved by the method of separation of variables:

$$\frac{dY(y)}{dy} = -\phi \ = \text{constant.}$$
$$\frac{dX(x)}{dx} = +\phi \ = \text{constant.}$$

With the following solutions:

$$Y = -\phi y + x_0 \ .$$

(3.5.5)

$$X = +\phi x + y_0 \,,$$

where (x_0, y_0) is a pair of integration constants.

Geometrical interpretation of the above result:

We have three degrees of freedom in the solution, which describe the infinitesimal group of motions of the bidimensional Euclidean space; these are the translations x_0 and y_0 along the axes OX and OY, and rotations around the origin $x = y = 0$ according to an angle arc sin ϕ.

3.7. Stationary and Static Fields

A gravitational field is said to be stationary if it admits a Killing temporal vector, i.e., $a_i a^i > 0$. From the Killing equation:

$$a_{i;j} + a_{j;i} = 0 \,,$$

where,

$$a_i = g_{ij} a^j \,.$$

We shall now investigate the above definition. We build a coordinate system such that only the coordinate x^0 varies along the trajectories of a^i keeping constant the space coordinates (x^1, x^2, x^3). In this system the trajectories of a^i are the self axis x^0, and $a^1 = a^2 = a^3 = 0$. On choosing a unit Killing vector,

$$a^i(x) \equiv (1, 0, 0, 0) \,,$$

we shall find Killing's equation reduced to:

$$a^i \frac{\partial g_{jk}}{\partial x^i} = a^0 \frac{\partial g_{jk}}{\partial x^0} = 0 \,, \text{ or,}$$

$$\boxed{\frac{\partial g_{jk}}{\partial x^0} = 0}$$

In the new coordinate system all the components of the metric tensor are time independent. We say that the coordinate system is adapted to the stationary character of the metric, i.e., it is adapted to the Killing vector field. Kerr's metric which describes a rotating body is an example of stationary metric.

Static Field

A given gravitation field is called static, if there exists a coordinate system adapted to the stationary character of the metric for which

Chapter 4

Basic Theory

4.1. The Basic Principles

Should a theory be "beautiful" in order to be acceptable? — In my subjective opinion, YES! For women, intelligence does the job. South American judges and politicians are usually clever; they get rich, but they are seldom intelligent or honest. Some are even crazy. Also, some scientists (but not me !). Let the ugly ones, forgive me, because for theories, beauty is fundamental. Honesty is supposed to be required from everybody.

General Relativity Theory is an intelligent theory of Gravitation, endowed with beautiful equations. It acknowledges that, in a given point of space, an accelerated system is equivalent to a local inertial one, subject to a gravitational field (Principle of Equivalence). This principle has experimental basis in E'otvös experiment, which suggests the equality between inertial and gravitational mass. In Newtonian Mechanics the origin of the inertial mass comes from the second Newton's Law (forces are proportional to accelerations; the constant of proportionality is inertial mass); gravitational mass, is the one which makes the weight of a body proportional to the acceleration of gravity (the constant of proportionality being the gravitational mass).

GRT obeys the covariance principle for the laws of Physics, as already commented. The father of the theory, Albert Einstein, tried to find equations for the motion of bodies in the presence of gravitational fields, which he expected to reduce to the known laws of Special Relativity, when the gravitational field would be switched off; and in the case of weak gravitational fields, and low speeds, when compared to the speed of light, Einstein expected that the GRT equations reduced to those of Newtonian gravitation.

We shall see later that a particle's acceleration in a gravitational field, is proportional to the Christoffel symbols. As it was shown in last chapter, it is always possible, by means of a coordinate transformation (to a geodesic system), to turn to zero the Christoffel symbols at a given point of spacetime. Then, in the new localized coordinate system, at that point, a body feels no acceleration: this makes sense with the Equivalence Principle. For more on "principles", we refer to Berman (2007; 2007a).

If the equation for matter fields, is written with the tensor T^{ij} obeying the above property and on remembering that in Riemannian geometry which has a similar law of conservation for the Einstein's tensor, namely

$$G^{ij}_{;j} = 0, \tag{4.4.2}$$

which we studied in Chapter 2, it would be reasonable that matter and geometry of space were tied by the equations

$$\boxed{G^{ij} = -\kappa T^{ij}} \qquad \text{(Einstein's field Equations)} \tag{4.4.3}$$

because then the properties (4.4.2) and (4.4.1) would be automatically fulfilled: we may say that matter makes the geometry. Precisely speaking, if we know the energy density and the pressure of a fluid, we may build its energy momentum tensor, and then we shall know how this matter curves spacetime through the Einstein tensor, which reflects the properties of the curvature of spacetime. The constant κ is called Einstein's gravitational constant and it is closely related to Newtonian gravitational constant G as we shall show later on. The plausibility for (4.4.3), lies in the paragraph following formula (4.4.5) below.

Einstein's field equations should reduce for weak gravitational fields and low speeds when compared with the speed of light, to the Newtonian equations of Poisson:

$$\frac{\partial^2 \Psi}{\partial x^v \partial x^v} = -4\pi G \rho \tag{4.4.4}$$

where Ψ is the Newtonian scalar potential, G is the Newton's gravitational constant and ρ stands for mass density, while the potential Ψ relates with Newton's second law by

$$\frac{d^2 x^v}{dt^2} = -\frac{\partial \Psi}{\partial x^v} \quad . \tag{4.4.5}$$

In order that this last expression is also verified we need an additional hypothesis: a particle subject to a gravitational field moves according to a timelike geodesic of Riemann's spacetime. Roughly speaking, we can say that we have found the following reduction, which yields (4.4.4) from (4.4.3):

$$\boxed{G^{ij} \rightarrow \frac{\partial^2 \Psi}{\partial x^v \partial x^v}} \qquad \text{while} \qquad \boxed{T^{ij} \rightarrow -\tfrac{1}{2}\kappa\rho} \quad .$$

In Chapter 3, section 3.2, we saw that the equation of geodesics expresses the fact that the tangent vector to the curve stays parallel to itself during motion.

The equation derived for geodesics in Riemann spaces is

$$\frac{d^2 x^i}{ds^2} + \Gamma^i_{jk} u^j u^k = 0 \quad . \tag{4.4.6}$$

Now, we shall show that geodesics reduce to straight lines of Euclidean geometry in the absence of gravitation. Indeed, if gravitation is absent we can choose Cartesian coordinates where the Christoffel symbols are null. We are left with the equation:

$$\frac{d^2 x^i}{ds^2} = 0.$$

For $i = 0$ we find

$$\frac{d^2 x^0}{ds^2} = 0$$

which has the solution $x^0 = s$. With this solution we find:

$$\frac{d^2 x^i}{dx_0^2} = 0 \quad \text{or}$$

$$\frac{d^2 x^i}{dt^2} = 0$$

which are the equations of a straight line. QED.

We remember that straight lines are the shortest curves between two points in Euclidean Geometry and that a similar rôle can be attached to geodesics in the Riemannian geometry (stationary property).

Einstein proposed, in the year 1916, that the geodesic postulate should be incorporated to GRT as a separate one. Eleven years later however, Einstein and Grommer showed that this postulate could be indeed demonstrated with help of the field equations alone. Nevertheless, there are some restrictions for the derivation of this postulate from the field equations; for instance, a spinning particle does not follow geodesics. (see details in Papapetrou, 1974 – Section 42).

In this Chapter, we shall offer a particular case ($p = 0$ matter , also called "dust"), where we shall show how to derive the equation of geodesics from field equations (4.4.3).

4.5. Introducing the Cosmological Constant

The Einstein tensor, G^{ij}, as we recall from Chapter 2, had the property that its covariant divergence was null. Because any tensor proportional to the metric tensor has zero covariant derivative we may say that any tensor of the type:

$$E^{ij} = G^{ij} + \Lambda g^{ij} \quad , \tag{4.5.1}$$

where Λ is an arbitrary constant, has also a null covariant divergence:

$$E^{ij}_{;j} = 0. \tag{4.5.2}$$

Albert Einstein furthermore concluded that his field equations should be conceived with the lambda constant, employing thus the tensor E^{ij} instead of G^{ij} so that we would find:

$$\boxed{E^{ij} = -\kappa T^{ij}} \tag{4.5.3}$$

We call the above field equations (4.5.3 as the field equations with a cosmological constant. The word "cosmological" is not without reason: for local Physics experiments we

On comparing (4.6.3) with the Newtonian equation:

$$\frac{d^2 x^i}{dt^2} = -\frac{\partial \Psi}{\partial x^i} \quad ,$$

we find that:

$$\Psi \approx \frac{g_{00} c^2}{2} + \text{constant} .$$

In order to determine the value of the constant above we shall consider Minkowski's metric, which is the limiting metric for points that are infinitely far from the masses. In this case:

$$g_{00} \rightarrow 1 \quad ,$$

$$\Psi \rightarrow 0 \quad ,$$

and then

$$\Psi = \frac{c^2}{2} + \text{constant} \rightarrow 0 ,$$

or,

$$\Psi = \frac{g_{00} c^2}{2} - \frac{c^2}{2} \quad ,$$

and then

$$g_{00} = 1 + \frac{2\Psi}{c^2} . \tag{4.6.4}$$

Therefore, g_{00} stands for a gravitational potential, and, consequently we justified in calling the metric tensor components as the "gravitational potentials". It is also clear from the intermediary step where we found,

$$\frac{d^2 x^i}{ds^2} \approx -\Gamma^i_{00} \quad ,$$

that the Christoffel symbols represent accelerations, as we had advanced earlier.

2nd Condition: Obtainment of the value for Einstein's gravitational constant.

In the same conditions as above we now undertake the calculation of curvature tensor components R^i_{jkl}. As the Christoffel symbols are very small quantities, their products are negligible. So we can write:

$$R^i_{jkl} \approx \frac{\partial \Gamma^i_{jl}}{\partial x^k} - \frac{\partial \Gamma^i_{jk}}{\partial x^l} \quad .$$

Therefore, we obtain Ricci tensor by:

$$R_{jk} \approx \frac{1}{2} \frac{\partial}{\partial x^k} \left[\frac{\partial \gamma_{ji}}{\partial x^i} + \frac{\partial \gamma_{ii}}{\partial x^j} - \frac{\partial \gamma_{ij}}{\partial x^i} \right] - \frac{1}{2} \frac{\partial}{\partial x^i} \left[\frac{\partial \gamma_{ij}}{\partial x^k} + \frac{\partial \gamma_{ki}}{\partial x^j} - \frac{\partial \gamma_{jk}}{\partial x^i} \right] =$$

$$\frac{1}{2} \left[\frac{\partial^2 \gamma_{ii}}{\partial x^j \partial x^k} + \frac{\partial^2 \gamma_{jk}}{\partial x^i \partial x^i} - \frac{\partial^2 \gamma_{ij}}{\partial x^i \partial x^k} - \frac{\partial^2 \gamma_{ki}}{\partial x^i \partial x^j} \right] \quad .$$

In the particular case $j = k = 0$, we obtain:

$$R_{00} \approx \frac{1}{2}\left[\frac{\partial^2 \gamma_{ii}}{\partial x^0 \partial x^0} + \frac{\partial^2 \gamma_{00}}{\partial x^i \partial x^i} - 2\frac{\partial^2 \gamma_{10}}{\partial x^i \partial x^0}\right] \quad .$$

In the static case,

$$R_{00} \approx \frac{1}{2}\frac{\partial^2 \gamma_{00}}{\partial x^i \partial x^i} \approx \frac{1}{2}\nabla^2 \gamma_{00} \approx \frac{1}{2}\nabla^2 g_{00} \quad .$$

In accordance with (4.6.4) the last expression reduces to:

$$R_{00} \approx \frac{1}{c^2}\nabla^2 \Psi . \tag{4.6.5}$$

We now are going to make a detour, and show that Einstein's field equations may be expressed, alternatively as

$$R_{ij} = \kappa \left[\frac{1}{2}g_{ij}T - T_{ij}\right] \quad , \tag{4.6.6}$$

where

$$T \equiv T_i^i \quad .$$

By contracting the (4.4.3) field equation, we obtain:

$$G_i^i = \kappa T_i^i \quad , \text{or}$$

$$R = \kappa T . \tag{4.6.7}$$

If we now plug (4.6.7) in equation (4.4.3), we obtain the desired relation (4.6.6).

After this detour, we return to (4.6.5) and we apply (4.6.6):

$$\frac{1}{c^2}\nabla^2 \Psi = \kappa \left(\frac{1}{2}g_{00}T - T_{00}\right) \quad . \tag{4.6.8}$$

We now suppose the absence of other fields like for instance the electromagnetic; we suppose altogether that the matter distribution is that of "dust", i.e., $p \cong 0$, or,

$$T^{ij} = \rho u^i u^j \quad .$$

In the static case we shall find:

$$T_{00} \cong \rho\left(g_{00}\right)^2 \cong \rho \quad ,$$

and

$$T \cong \rho\left(g_{00}\right)^2 \cong \rho \quad .$$

On taking this values into (4.6.8), we obtain,

Chapter 5

Schwarzschild's Metric and Classical Experimental Tests

5.1. Spherically Symmetric Metrics

We define a metric with spherical symmetry around the origin, as a metric which is form-invariant according to the group of orthogonal transformations, of the type:

$$\widetilde{X} = AX \ ,$$

where,

$$X \equiv (x, y, z) \ ,$$

$$\widetilde{X} \equiv (\widetilde{x}, \widetilde{y}, \widetilde{z}) \ ,$$

and

$$AA^T = I \ ,$$

where I represents the identity matrix. (For the reader who needs to know, and does not, what are orthogonal transformations, next chapter has a review on it).

A metric is form-invariant if, in a transformation of coordinates $X \to \widetilde{X}$, we have,

$$g_{ij}(x) = \widetilde{g}_{ij}(\widetilde{x}) \ .$$

Notice that the temporal coordinate is excluded from this spherical symmetry definition.

Form-invariants, for this group of transformations, are the following, up to second order in the coordinate differentials:

$$+x^2 + y^2 + z^2 \ ,$$

$$+x dx + y dy + z dz \ ,$$

$$+dx^2 + dy^2 + dz^2 \ .$$

In spherical coordinates (r, θ, ϕ), the above invariants become:

$$+r^2 \, ,$$

$$+rdr \, ,$$

$$+d\theta^2 + \sin^2 \theta d\phi^2 \, .$$

We may also conclude, that the following are invariants: ($r, dr, d\theta^2, + \sin^2 \theta d\phi^2$). In this way, the most general spherically symmetric metric in Riemann four-dimensional space (r, θ, ϕ, t) is:

$$ds^2 = A(r,t)dr^2 + B(r,t)(d\theta^2 + \sin^2 \theta d\phi^2) + C(r,t)drdt + D(r,t)dt^2 \, , \qquad (5.1.1)$$

where the four coefficients A, B, C, D are up to now completely arbitrary.

Now let us remember Minkowski's metric:

$$ds^2 = -dx^\nu dx^\nu + c^2 dt^2. \qquad\qquad (\nu = 1, 2, 3)$$

In spherical coordinates, Minkowski's metric may therefore be expressed by:

$$ds^2 = -dr^2 - r^2(d\theta^2 + \sin^2 \theta d\phi^2) + c^2 dt^2 \, . \qquad (5.1.2)$$

The metric which represents a mass distribution in the origin, should reduce, when the radial coordinate becomes very large ($r \to \infty$), to the Minkowski's metric; (in Cosmology, this may not be alike), so we take:

$$B(r,t) = r^2 \, .$$

In the case of a static gravitational field, the functions $A(r,t)$, $C(r,t)$, and $D(r,t)$ should not depend on the time coordinate t. On the other hand, the time dependence of the metric should be symmetric; i.e., the form of the metric can not be altered by a transformation $t \to -t$: we conclude that $C = 0$. We are left with the following metric:

$$ds^2 = - \left[e^{\alpha(r)}dr^2 + r^2(d\theta^2 + \sin^2 \theta d\phi^2) \right] + e^{\beta(r)}c^2 dt^2 \, .$$

We choose in the above expression for the metric the exponentials $e^{\alpha(r)}$ and $e^{\beta(r)}$ so that they remain essentially positive and the signature of the metric should not change, at least for the time being.

We now begin the calculation of the metric tensor, the Christoffel symbols and the curvature and Ricci tensors, while attaching the following correspondence:

$$(x^0, x^1, x^2, x^3) \equiv (t, r, \theta, \phi) \quad .$$

1st) Non-null covariant metric tensor components:

$$g_{11} = -e^\alpha \quad ,$$

$$g_{22} = -r^2 \quad ,$$

$$g_{33} = -r^2 \sin^2 \theta \, ,$$

$$g_{00} = e^\beta c^2 \quad ,$$

$$g = det(g_{ij}) = -e^{(\alpha+\beta)} c^2 r^4 \sin^2 \theta \, .$$

2nd) Non-null contravariant components of the metric tensor:

$$g^{11} = -\frac{1}{e^\alpha} = -e^{-\alpha} \, ,$$

$$g^{22} = -\frac{1}{r^2} \, ,$$

$$g^{33} = -\frac{1}{r^2 \sin^2 \theta} \, ,$$

$$g^{00} = -\frac{1}{e^\beta c^2} .$$

3rd) Non-null Christoffel symbols of the second kind:

$$\Gamma_{11}^1 = \frac{\alpha'}{2} \, ,$$

$$\Gamma_{12}^2 = \Gamma_{21}^2 = \frac{1}{r} \, ,$$

$$\Gamma_{13}^3 = \Gamma_{31}^3 = \frac{1}{r} \, ,$$

$$\Gamma_{10}^0 = \Gamma_{01}^0 = \frac{\beta'}{2} \, ,$$

$$\Gamma_{22}^1 = -re^{-\alpha} \, ,$$

$$\Gamma_{23}^3 = \Gamma_{32}^3 = \cotg \, \theta \, ,$$

$$\Gamma_{33}^1 = -re^{-\alpha} \sin^2 \theta \, ,$$

$$\Gamma_{33}^2 = -\sin \theta \cos \theta ,$$

$$\Gamma^1_{00} = -\tfrac{1}{2} c^2 \beta' e^{(\beta - \alpha)} \ .$$

(the primes indicate derivatives in relation to the radial coordinate).

4th) Ricci tensor non-null components:

$$R_{11} = \frac{\beta''}{2} + \frac{\beta'^2}{4} - \frac{\alpha'\beta'}{4} - \frac{\alpha'}{r} \ ,$$
$$R_{22} = e^{-\alpha} \left[r\frac{\beta'}{2} - \frac{r\alpha'}{2} + 1 \right] - 1.$$

$$R_{33} = R_{22} \sin^2 \theta \ .$$

$$R_{00} = c^2 e^{(\beta - \alpha)} \left[-\tfrac{1}{2}\beta'' - \tfrac{1}{4}\beta'^2 + \tfrac{1}{4}\alpha'\beta' - \frac{\beta'}{r} \right] \ .$$

Schwarzschild's metric exterior solution

The metric obtained by us, shall be certainly a solution for a static distribution, with spherical symmetry around the origin. For points that are exterior to the mass distribution in the origin, Einstein's field equations reduce to:

$$R_{ij} = 0 \ , \tag{5.1.4}$$

because $T_{ij} = 0$.

According to the above calculation, we are left with the equations:

$$\beta'' + \tfrac{1}{2}\beta'^2 - \tfrac{1}{2}\alpha'\beta' - \tfrac{2}{r}\alpha' = 0 \ , \tag{5.1.5}$$

$$\tfrac{1}{2}\beta'r - \tfrac{1}{2}\alpha'r + 1 = e^{\alpha} \ , \tag{5.1.6}$$

$$\beta'' + \tfrac{1}{2}\beta'^2 - \tfrac{1}{2}\alpha'\beta' - \tfrac{2}{r}\beta' = 0 \ . \tag{5.1.7}$$

Notice that we were left with three independent equations alone, because in our case,

$R_{22} = 0 \to R_{33} = 0$.

By comparing (5.1.5) and (5.1.7), we obtain:

$$\alpha + \beta = \text{constant.} \tag{5.1.8}$$

The above equality should also be valid in spatial infinity where it should be identified by the values in the Minkowski's metric (5.1.2), and

$$e^{\alpha} = e^{\beta} = 1 \qquad \therefore \qquad \alpha \equiv \beta = 0 \ .$$

The constant in (5.1.8) is obviously zero-valued. And then, we find:

$$\alpha = -\beta \quad \text{at any place .} \tag{5.1.9}$$

From (5.1.6) we now obtain

$$r\alpha' = 1 - e^{\alpha} \quad ,$$

or in other words,

$$\frac{dr}{r} = \frac{d\alpha}{1-e^{\alpha}} \quad .$$

When we integrate, the above equation, and we call "m" a constant of integration, we find:

$$e^{\alpha} = \frac{1}{1-\frac{2m}{r}} \quad . \tag{5.1.10}$$

Then

$$e^{\beta} = 1 - \frac{2m}{r} \quad . \tag{5.1.11}$$

We have thus obtained Schwarzschild's metric:

$$ds^2 = \frac{-dr^2}{1-\frac{2m}{r}} - r^2(d\theta^2 + \sin^2\theta d\phi^2) + c^2(1 - \frac{2m}{r})dt^2 \quad . \tag{5.1.12}$$

The integration constant "m" can be given now a precise value: we remember that very far from the origin, where the mass M is located, the above metric can be identified with the metric of a weak field whose temporal metric coefficient is given by (4.5.4):

$$g_{00} = 1 + \frac{2\Psi}{c^2} \quad . \tag{4.5.4}$$

We conjecture that the potential Ψ very far from the origin, is given by its Newtonian expression namely :

$$\Psi = -\frac{GM}{r} \quad . \tag{5.1.13}$$

Obviously, we can identify the integration constant "m" with:

$$m = \frac{GM}{c^2} \quad . \tag{5.1.14}$$

There is an apparent singularity of the Schwarzschild's metric for the point:

$$r = 2m = \frac{2GM}{c^2} \quad . \tag{5.1.15}$$

This radial distance is called Schwarzschild's radius, and its value for the Earth, is about 9mm. If the Earth's mass would be entirely concentrated inside a sphere of radius smaller then 9mm, we would have a **black-hole**. By the so called process of gravitational collapse, its radius would become even more smaller than that, though I hope that it should not reduce to an infinitesimally small point of zero radius. Through the Schwarzschild's metric, a white-hole can also be envisaged with properties similar to a fountain of matter and photons surging from an apparent point-like source (see Part III).

3rd Law: The sum of Kinetic plus potential energy is conserved.

$$\left(\frac{dr}{dt}\right)^2 + r^2\left(\frac{d\phi}{dt}\right)^2 - \frac{2GM}{r} = h' = \text{constant}. \tag{5.2.13}$$

For the comparison between GRT and Newtonian Mechanics results to be effective, we remember that in Newtonian Mechanics the proper time confounds itself with time "t" so that for the Newtonian metric we can write:

$$ds = cdt\ . \tag{5.2.14}$$

On a comparison we identify:

$$m = \frac{GM}{c^2}.$$

This result confirms the derivation done in Section 5.1 (Formula (5.1.14)).

In Newtonian Mechanics, the solution for (5.2.12) and (5.2.13) is straightforward:

$$\frac{d^2u}{d\phi^2} + u = \frac{GM}{C^2}\ , \tag{5.2.15}$$

where

$$u = \frac{1}{r}.$$

The Newtonian solution is a conic, given by:

$$u_N = \frac{1}{r} = \frac{GM}{C^2}\left[1 + e\cos\phi\right], \tag{5.2.16}$$

where e stands for the eccentricity of the conic.

We now return to the relativistic equations which for our purpose of comparison can be written as:

$$\frac{dr}{ds} = \frac{dr}{d\phi}\frac{d\phi}{ds} = \frac{dr}{d\phi}\frac{C}{r^2} = -C\frac{du}{d\phi}\ , \tag{5.2.17}$$

and,

$$\left(\frac{du}{d\phi}\right)^2 + 2u\frac{du}{d\phi} - \frac{2m}{C^2}\frac{du}{d\phi} - 6mu^2\frac{du}{d\phi} = 0\ . \tag{5.2.18}$$

Differentiating the last equation in relation to ϕ , and applying equation (5.2.17), we obtain:

$$\frac{d^2u}{d\phi^2} + u = \frac{m}{C^2} + 3mu^2\ \ . \tag{5.2.19}$$

On comparison with (5.2.14) we identify:

$$\frac{m}{C^2} = \frac{GM}{C^2}\ .$$

The additional relativistic term,

$$3mu^2 = \frac{3GM}{c^2}\frac{1}{r^2} \quad ,$$

turns out to be much smaller than the other terms, so it is a "perturbative" term.

We know then, that the relativistic orbit of the planet can only have a small deviation from an ellipse which is the Newtonian basic solution. In the perturbative term, we plug tentatively the Newtonian solution for the ellipse, u_N , so we write:

$$\frac{d^2u}{d\phi^2} + u \cong \frac{m}{C^2} + 3m(u_N)^2 \quad . \tag{5.2.20}$$

It is evident that the solution of the above equation must render a better approximation than the solution:

$$u \cong u_N \ ,$$

for the equation (5.2.20).

We now substitute u_N by the value given in (5.2.16) and plug into (5.2.20); we make the approximation $e^2 << 1$, and find :

$$\frac{d^2u}{d\phi^2} + u = \frac{m}{C^2} + \frac{6m^3}{C^4}e\cos\phi, \tag{5.2.21}$$

where we also considered:

$$\frac{3m^2}{C^2} << 1 \ .$$

The solution to the above equation is:

$$u = \frac{1}{r} = \frac{m}{C^2}\left[1 + e\cos\left(\phi - \frac{3m^2}{C^2}\phi\right)\right] \quad . \tag{5.2.22}$$

On comparison between (5.2.22) and (5.2.16), we verify that there is an advance in the principal axis of the ellipse, which for a round turn ($\Delta\phi = 2\pi$) is given by:

$$\Delta\omega = \frac{6\pi m^2}{C^2} \quad .$$

On the other hand, if we call "a" the semi major axis of the ellipse,

$$\frac{C^2}{m} = a(1 - e^2) \quad .$$

This is tantamount to:

$$\therefore \quad \boxed{\Delta\omega = \frac{6\pi GM}{c^2 a(1-e^2)}} \ . \tag{5.2.23}$$

For the planet Mercury,

$$\Delta w \simeq 0,104''.$$

In one century the calculated advance would be 43,0" as compared to the experimental value, from astronomical observations, 43,1".

We can not forget that the total advance in the perihelion of the planet Mercury is 5,600". The non-relativistic perturbations accounted by the interference of other planets' orbits accounts for 5,557" and only 43,41" are explained by GRT corrections, not justified in Newtonian Mechanics. This match was perhaps the most astonishing result of Albert Einstein's theory, and testifies in favor of GRT.

5.3. Propagation of Light near Gravitational Fields

In Special Relativity Theory the light trajectory is given by:

$$ds = 0 \ .$$

Though this result is a bit obvious we shall demonstrate it for the sake of completeness, and because many beginning students do not find it explicit from some textbooks.

We recall Minkowski's metric:

$$ds^2 = - \left[dx^2 + dy^2 + dz^2 \right] + c^2 dt^2 \ . \tag{2.1.4}$$

If the speed of a particle is defined kinematically as:

$$V = \sqrt{dx^2 + dy^2 + dz^2} / dt \ ,$$

and we apply this formula for a photon, we know that the result is $V = c$. Plugging back into (2.1.4) we find $ds = 0$. A result valid for photons and thus for light rays. When we go to GRT we are led to keep the equation for light rays as:

$$ds = 0 \ . \tag{5.3.1}$$

For a photon in the neighborhood of a central mass M located at the origin of the co-ordinate system with a spherically symmetric distribution, we take Schwarzschild's metric, and the equations (5.2.19) and (5.2.11) can be kept along with (5.3.1). In our case the value of the constant C which appears in (5.2.11) is to be taken, obviously, as infinite:

$$C = \infty. \tag{5.3.2}$$

This being the case we are left from (5.2.19) with:

$$\frac{d^2u}{d\phi^2} + u = 3mu^2 \cdot \tag{5.3.3}$$

We take into account that the r.h.s. of (5.3.3) represents a small corrective or perturbative term, in the case of the Sun for example. In that case, $u = \frac{1}{r}$ would be calculated with r equal to the Sun's radius, and it is clear that the approximate solution of this equation would be $u \cong u_1$, where u_1 stands in the equation:

$$\frac{d^2u_1}{d\phi^2} + u_1 \cong 0 \, .$$

Its solution is:

$$u_1 = \frac{\cos\phi}{R} \, ,$$

where R stands for a constant.

A better approximation may now be obtainable by solving the following equation:

$$\frac{d^2u}{d\phi^2} + u = 3m(u_1)^2 = \frac{3m\cos^2\phi}{R^2} \tag{5.3.4}$$

The reader should pay attention and focus himself that the above equation (5.3.4) comes in fact from (5.3.3) where in r.h.s. we have substituted u by its Newtonian solution.

The solution of (5.3.4) is

$$u = \frac{1}{R}\cos\phi + \frac{m}{R^2}\left(2 - \cos^2\phi\right).$$

The equation which one finds for the deviation of light rays in the neighborhood of a central gravitational mass like the Sun, is obtainable if we compare the two farthest rays for which:

$$u = \frac{1}{r} = 0 \, .$$

We have an equation of the second degree in $\cos\phi$:

$$(m/R)\cos^2\phi - \cos\phi - (2m/R) = 0.$$

Its roots are:

$$\cos\phi = \left[1 \pm \sqrt{1 + \frac{8m^2}{R^2}}\right](2m/R)^{-1} \, .$$

In our approximation:

$$\frac{m^2}{R^2} << 1 \, .$$

We now find:

$$\cos\phi \cong \left[1 \pm \left(1 + \frac{4m^2}{R^2}\right)\right](2m/R)^{-1} \, .$$

The first solution is:

$$\cos\phi \cong (2m/R) \, .$$

The second solution is:

$$\cos\phi' \cong \left(2 + \frac{4m^2}{R^2}\right)(2m/R)^{-1} = \frac{R}{m} + \frac{2m}{R} \, .$$

2nd) Hafele-Keating experiment:

In Section 5.4 we mentioned the relation between proper time $d\tau_1$ and coordinate time dt for Schwarzschild's metric:

$$d\tau_1 = \sqrt{1 - \frac{2m}{R}} dt ,$$ (5.5.1)

in the presence of a gravitational field. On the other hand, in Special Relativity there is a second variation between proper time $d\tau_2$ and the coordinate time dt for a moving object with speed v :

$$d\tau_2 = \sqrt{1 - v^2/c^2} dt .$$ (5.5.2)

Equation (5.5.1) tells us that clocks go slower in the presence of strong gravitational fields. Relation (5.5.2) tells us that clocks go faster when they move, relative to static clocks. By means of Hafele-Keating experiment it was possible to compare clocks readings inside airplanes with similar clocks on the Earth's surface. A team of the University of Maryland in the United States, made measurements between the years 1975 and 1976. Due to differences in the intensity of the gravitational fields on the Earth's surface, and the flying airplanes it was found an advancement in time measured by the clocks inside airplanes according to (5.5.2). However, this effect was partially camouflaged by the opposite effect due to the speed of the airplanes relative to static clocks on the Earth's surface. By employing slow motion airplanes, this opposite effect was reduced to less than 10% of the total retardation; thus formula (5.5.1) could be verified experimentally with 98% of precision relative to the theoretical value.

3rd) Shapiro experiment:

In the year 1965, the American scientist I. I. Shapiro proposed the following experiment: a radar wave emission should be directed to another planet so that the light ray would pass near the Sun. The planet would reflect the radar emission, the time lag would be measured and obviously the time taken would be larger than expected due to the passage near the Sun. In the year 1970 Shapiro made the measurement confirming Einstein's theory with 97% of accuracy.

4th) Hulse-Taylor observations:

As we mentioned in last Chapter, GRT's predictions of the existence of gravitational waves, got indirect confirmation by means of the observation of a Pulsar, with a possible companion; they would loose energy due to gravitational radiation according to the general relativistic calculation (Einstein's formula), not derived or shown in this book.

Note on gravitational radiation: it is my opinion that gravitational waves' direct detection, may be hindered by a misleading interpretation of the tensors formulae; there is a great difference between "tensor components", and "physical tensor components". The latter, are the ones that are experimentally measured, and they may be affecting the order of magnitude of the sought slight relative displacement on the detectors. (Synge and Schild, 1969).

5th) Global Positioning System (GPS) — NAVSTAR :

By continuously emitting radio waves, at fixed frequencies, several orbiting satellites can active a GPS detector, (for instance, inside an airplane), which arrive with a Doppler shift, dependent on the relative speed of the source and the receiver; it also depends on the gravitational potential difference between the locations of the source and receiver. Both Special and General Relativity are involved; speeds and positions of the airplanes are then measured with extreme accuracy (± 2 cm.s^{-1} ; 16 m). This system of navigation is called GPS-NAVSTAR, and works well.

Final Comments

Einstein has commented that it would suffice a single negative result breaking GRT's predictions, in order that this theory be discarded, despite all positives other confirmatory results.

Chapter 6

Simple "Derivation" of Black Holes' Metrics

6.1. New "Derivation" of Einstein's Field Equations

Shortly after the appearance of Einstein's General Relativistic field equations, the first static and spherically symmetric solution became available: it was Schwarzschild's metric (Schwarzschild, 1916). It described the gravitational field around a point like mass M. Afterwards, the first rotational metric was developed: Lense-Thirring solution (Thirring and Lense, 1918). It described the field around a rotating sphere at the origin. Nevertheless, it was only an approximate solution, that only represented a weak field, in the slow rotation case. Reissner and Nordström's metric (Reissner, 1916), generalized Schwarzschild's by charging the mass source in the origin. It was only in the sixties of last century, that a rigorous solution representing the rotation of a central mass, was discovered by Roy Kerr, in what is now called Kerr's metric (Kerr, 1963). Immediately afterwards, the generalization to a charged rotating central mass was supplied, which is now called Kerr-Newman's metric (Newman et al. 1965).

The literature on black holes is, by now, very extensive. In recent times, some elementary books have appeared, which intend to teach beginners without using thoroughly, its natural tool, i.e., tensor calculus. (For instance: Taylor and Wheeler, 2000; or, Raine and Thomas, 2005). Nevertheless, it has been lacking a simple derivation of any of those metrics, without the use of sophisticated mathematics. Taylor and Wheeler (2000) refer to an article about the impossibility of a simple derivation of the Schwarzschild's metric (Gruber et al., 1988). While preparing this textbook, I have made some elementary derivations, now being presented here (see next Sections).

Before going to Black Hole metrics, we shall consider again the "derivation" of Einstein's field equations, this time considering the Geodesic deviation equation (see Section 2.7).

From Newtonian theory, considering two neighboring particles in free fall, outside a mass distribution which generates a gravitational field. For the two particles, we write their respective accelerations in terms of the potential:

$$\vec{a}_1 = -\nabla\phi_1 , \tag{6.1.1}$$

and,
$$\vec{a}_2 = -\nabla\phi_2 . \tag{6.1.2}$$

The relative displacement vector, $\vec{r}$, will vary like,

$$\vec{a}_r = \frac{d^2\vec{r}}{dt^2} = \nabla\phi_2 - \nabla\phi_1. \tag{6.1.3}$$

The corresponding scalar equation is,

$$\frac{d^2r}{dt^2} = \frac{\partial^2}{\partial r^2}\left(\phi_2 - \phi_1\right) . \tag{6.1.4}$$

The exterior equation, in Newtonian theory, is obtained by plugging $\rho = 0$ in Poisson's equation, where ρ is mass density; we find Laplace's equation:

$$\nabla^2\phi = 0 . \tag{6.1.5}$$

From (6.1.4) and (6.1.5), we find:

$$\frac{d^2r}{dt^2} = 0 . \tag{6.1.6}$$

When we transfer from Newtonian Mechanics towards Special Relativity Theory, we must substitute coordinate time by proper time (see 2.6.5) :

$$\frac{d^2r}{d\tau^2} = 0 \tag{6.1.7}$$

Now we transfer again, this time from flat Euclidean space, towards Riemannian Geometry's curved space, and then, instead of (6.1.7), we must write:

$$\frac{D^2V^\alpha}{Ds^2} = 0 , \tag{6.1.8}$$

where we employed the notation used in Section 2.7. From equation (2.7.14), we know that this result (6.1.8), implies that the Riemann-Christoffel tensor has null components:

$$R^\alpha_{\mu\beta\nu} = 0 . \tag{6.1.9}$$

Einstein's tensor, is then, also null:

$$G_{\mu\nu} = 0 . \tag{6.1.10}$$

When we have an interior field equations, i.e., the field equations inside matter, we find, from the Newtonian counterpart, Poisson's equation, which makes the l.h.s. of equation (6.1.6), be proportional to ρ , and then, from the geodesic deviation equation, we learn that at least one particular component of Einstein's tensor, say $(\mu , \nu) = (\bar{\mu} , \bar{\nu})$, to be different from zero, at least in a small neighborhood of a certain point:

$$G_{\mu\nu} \neq 0 \quad (\text{for } \mu = \bar{\mu} \text{ and } \nu = \bar{\nu}). \tag{6.1.11}$$

We shall not deal with our "derivation" as in Section 3.4, but we refer back the reader to that Section. Instead, we point out, that having in mind Poisson's equation, we may say that $G_{\mu\nu}$ must have the non-zero component, somehow proportional to ρ. From Special Relativity, this ρ stands now for energy density; in that theory, this is again proportional to the zero-zero component of the energy momentum tensor. As we expect, we shall find the field equations inside matter, by equating Einstein's tensor, with a term proportional to the energy momentum tensor. Again, we are not proving anything; we are "guessing", or, at most, hinting to a possible set of field equations. The ultimate "proof", lies, perhaps, in the realm of experimental Gravitation, or, maybe in a possible explanation based on variational principles, found suitable to describe Gravitation.

6.2. "Derivation" of Schwarzschild's Metric

From Special Relativity, we know that in the absence of gravitation, the metric is given by:

$$ds^2 = c^2 dt^2 - d\sigma^2 = c^2 dt^2 - dx^2 - dy^2 - dz^2 = c^2 dt^2 - dr^2 - r^2 d\Omega , \tag{6.2.1}$$

where,

$$d\Omega = d\theta^2 + \sin^2\theta \; d\phi^2 . \tag{6.2.2}$$

In the above, (x, y, z) and (r, θ, ϕ) are Cartesian and spherical coordinates, respectively.

When a gravitational field appears, the metric is "curved", but in the static, spherically symmetric case, we can write generally that:

$$ds^2 = g_{00} c^2 dt^2 - g_{rr} dr^2 - r^2 d\Omega , \tag{6.2.3}$$

where, g_{00} and g_{rr} should be functions depending on the mass M and the radial coordinate r.

In order to estimate the first function, we consider a fixed event $(dr = d\theta = d\phi = 0)$. In this case, the proper time is given by $ds^2 \equiv d\tau^2$:

$$d\tau^2 = g_{00} c^2 dt^2. \tag{6.2.4}$$

In the above, dt represents coordinate time, i.e., the time far from the central mass distribution (call it, the time for a clock at infinity). From the Principle of Equivalence, we know that the relation between coordinate time, and the proper time, as measured close to a mass distribution, is given by (Sexl and Sexl, 1979) :

$$d\tau \cong \frac{dt}{\left[1 + \frac{GM}{c^2 R}\right]} = \frac{dt}{\left[1 - \frac{\Delta U}{c^2}\right]} . \tag{6.2.5}$$

On squaring the last expression, we find:

6.3. Isotropic Form of Schwarzschild's Metric

It is desirable that Schwarzschild's metric be cast in the isotropic form, which is meant by:

$$ds^2 = g_{00}c^2dt^2 - g_{\sigma\sigma}\,d\sigma^2\,. \qquad (6.3.1)$$

In order to find the correct isotropic form, we imagine that we make a change in coordinates, from R to ρ, and that we wish to find the relation between both, so that, when we begin with the standard Schwarzschild's metric (6.2.11), we find the isotropic metric:

$$ds^2 \cong \left[1 - \frac{2GM}{c^2\rho}\right]c^2dt^2 - \left[1 + \frac{2GM}{c^2\rho}\right]d\sigma^2, \qquad (6.3.2)$$

with,

$$d\sigma^2 = d\rho^2 + \rho^2 d\Omega. \qquad (6.3.3)$$

We took the $g_{00} = g_{00}(\rho)$ to be the same function as $g_{00}(R)$; it could work or not. In fact, it works.

We go right to the solution of the problem:

$$R \cong \left[1 + \frac{2GM}{c^2\rho}\right]^{\frac{1}{2}}\rho \cong \left[1 + \frac{GM}{c^2\rho}\right]\rho \cong \rho + \frac{GM}{c^2}. \qquad (6.3.4)$$

With the above substitution, in the metric (6.3.2), we obtain,

$$ds^2 = \left[1 - \frac{2GM}{c^2\rho}\right]c^2dt^2 - \left[1 + \frac{2GM}{c^2\rho}\right]\left[d\rho^2 + \rho^2 d\Omega\right]. \qquad (6.3.5)$$

In the same level of approximation, the last form of the metric, is indistinguishable from the following one, which is the exact isotropic form of Schwarzschild's metric:

$$ds^2 = \frac{\left[1 - \frac{GM}{2c^2\rho}\right]^2}{\left[1 + \frac{GM}{2c^2\rho}\right]^2}c^2dt^2 - \left[1 + \frac{GM}{2c^2\rho}\right]^4\left[d\rho^2 + \rho^2 d\Omega\right], \qquad (6.3.6)$$

6.4. "Derivation" of Lense-Thirring Metric

For a rotating central mass, we start first with the approximate isotropic metric of last Section (relation 6.3.5):

$$ds^2 = \left[1 - \frac{2GM}{c^2\rho}\right]c^2dt^2 - \left[1 + \frac{2GM}{c^2\rho}\right]\left[d\rho^2 + \rho^2 d\Omega\right]. \qquad (6.4.1)$$

Consider now a transformation from the above spherical coordinates, ρ, θ, ϕ, to a rotating frame, defined by the new coordinates R, θ, $\tilde{\phi}$, whereby:

$$R = \rho\,, \qquad (6.4.2a)$$

$$\tilde{\phi} = \phi - \omega\, t, \qquad (6.4.2b)$$

$$d\tilde{\phi} = d\phi - \omega\, dt. \qquad (6.4.2c)$$

The new expression for the metric, will be:

$$ds^2 = \left[1 - 2U - (1 + 2U)\,\omega^2 R^2 \sin^2\theta\right] c^2 dt^2 - (1 + 2U)\, d\sigma^2 + 2(1 + 2U)\,\omega R^2 \sin^2\theta\, d\phi\, dt\ , \quad (6.4.3)$$

where,

$$U = \frac{GM}{c^2 R}\ . \qquad (6.4.4)$$

Note that we have dropped the tilde from ϕ .

Consider now the greatest difference between the last metric and the non-rotating one, i.e., the existence of a non-diagonal metric element,

$$2(1 + 2U)\,\omega R^2 \sin^2\theta\, d\phi\, dt\ . \qquad (6.4.5)$$

We can define a Newtonian angular momentum J , so that:

$$2(1 + 2U)\,\omega R^2 \sin^2\theta\, d\phi\, dt = 2(1 + 2U)\,\tfrac{J}{M}\, d\phi\, dt\ . \qquad (6.4.6)$$

It is easy to check that we have employed a natural definition for J , in the above equation. As U and J , are small, so that the rotating metric is very approximately similar to the non-rotating one, we may also write:

$$g_{\phi t}\, d\phi\, dt = 2(1 + 2U)\,\omega R^2 \sin^2\theta\, d\phi\, dt = (1 + 2U)\,\tfrac{J}{M}\, d\phi\, dt \cong \left[\tfrac{2J}{M} + \tfrac{4GJ}{R}\right] d\phi\, dt\ . \qquad (6.4.7)$$

By the same token, the extra term in g_{00} , is given by the product of ω with the non-diagonal metric coefficient $g_{\phi t}$, i.e.,

$$\omega\left[\tfrac{J}{M} + \tfrac{2GJ}{R}\right]\ , \qquad (6.4.8)$$

which can be neglected, for being a second order infinitesimal.

The above results constitute the Lense-Thirring metric, which we now have shown to be derived with simple mathematics.

where Δ, ρ, and a are defined by:

$$\Delta \equiv r^2 - 2mr + a^2 , \tag{6.6.5}$$

$$\rho^2 \equiv r^2 + a^2 \cos^2\theta . \tag{6.6.6}$$

$$a^2 \equiv \frac{J^2}{M^2} . \tag{6.6.7}$$

The Kerr metric above is given in Boyer-Lindquist form.

We note again that we have induced and not derived the correct generalization of L.T. metric into (6.6.4), which is valid for any value of the rotation parameter.

Derivations of Alternative Forms for Kerr Metric

Following D'Inverno (1992), we shall now show how to derive the other two forms of Kerr metric (Boyer-Lindquist, and quasi-Cartesian, forms), beginning with Eddington-Finkelstein's one.

It will be shown that this metric, which we will keep as an additional information for completeness, is equivalent to the other two forms, and which we have "induced", but not derived.

$$ds^2 = \left(1 - \frac{2mr}{\rho^2}\right) dv^2 - 2dvdr + \frac{4mar}{\rho^2}\sin^2\theta dv \, d\bar{\phi} + 2a\sin^2\theta dr \, d\bar{\phi} - \rho^2 d\theta^2 - Ed\bar{\phi}^2, \tag{6.6.8}$$

where,

$$E = \left[(r^2 + a^2)\sin^2\theta + 2ma^2r\rho^{-2}\sin^2\theta\right] , \tag{6.6.9}$$

while, from (6.6.6), which we repeat here, we have,

$$\rho^2 \equiv r^2 + (a\cos\theta)^2 . \tag{6.6.6}$$

In order to make comparisons, with Schwarzschild's metric, we substitute the set of coordinates (v, r, θ, ϕ) by the set (t, r, θ, ϕ), where we find the correspondence among the two sets, from the implicit differential relations below:

$$dv = d\bar{t} + dr = dt + \left(\frac{2mr + \Delta}{\Delta}\right) dr , \tag{6.6.10}$$

and,

$$d\bar{\phi} = d\phi + \frac{a}{\Delta}dr , \tag{6.6.11}$$

taken care of (6.6.5).

With the above transformation we find, Boyer-Linquist's Kerr-metric (6.6.4).

Now, we employ quasi-Cartesian coordinates, by making the transformation contained in the following relations, between the set (v, r, θ, ϕ) and (t, x, y, z):

$$t = v - r. \tag{6.6.12}$$

$$x = r \sin^2 \theta \cos \phi + a \sin \theta \sin \phi. \tag{6.6.13}$$

$$y = r \sin \theta \sin \phi - a \sin \theta \cos \phi. \tag{6.6.14}$$

$$z = r \cos \theta. \tag{6.6.15}$$

We remark that, when $a = 0$, we obtain the Classical relationship between Cartesian and spherical coordinates, hence the name "quasi-Cartesian", of this form, which is given by (Newman et al., 1965):

$$ds^2 = dt^2 - dx^2 - dy^2 - dz^2 - \frac{2\left[M - \frac{Q^2}{2r_0}\right] r_0^3}{r_0^4 + a^2 z^2} \cdot F^2, \tag{6.6.16}$$

$$F = dt + \frac{z}{r_0} dz + \frac{r_0}{(r_0^2 + a^2)} (x \, dx + y \, dy) + \frac{a(x \, dy - y \, dx)}{a^2 + r_0^2}, \tag{6.6.17}$$

$$r_0^4 - (r^2 - a^2) r_0^2 - a^2 z^2 = 0, \tag{6.6.18}$$

and

$$r^2 \equiv x^2 + y^2 + z^2. \tag{6.6.19}$$

We have included a constant Q which is null in Kerr's metric (6.6.16), but which represents an electric charge, as in next Section.

The limiting cases of Kerr metric are:

A) Schwarzschild's metric: we recover this metric in the limit $a \to 0$.

B) Minkowski's metric: we recover when $m \to 0$ and $a \to 0$.

C) Minkowski's rotating Universe: when $m \to 0$ but $a \neq 0$.

D) Lense-Thirring metric: when $a^2 \ll 1$.

In order to check the limiting case of a Minkowski's rotating metric, we may proceed afresh like it follows. We write:

$$ds^2 = dt^2 - dx^2 - dy^2 - dz^2.$$

In cylindrical coordinates, the above metric would become:

$$d\tilde{s}^2 = dt^2 - \left[d\tilde{r}^2 + \tilde{r}^2 d\tilde{\phi}^2 + d\tilde{z}^2\right].$$

where

$$h \equiv h_\gamma^\gamma \, , \tag{6.8.4}$$

and,

$$\Box^2 \equiv \frac{\partial^2}{\partial t^2} - \nabla^2 \, . \tag{6.8.5}$$

$\Box^2$ and ∇^2 stand respectively for the d'Alembertian and 3-dimensional Laplacian in Minkowski space. The curvature scalar is, now:

$$R = h_{,\gamma\delta}^{\gamma\delta} - \Box^2 h \, , \tag{6.8.6}$$

With appropriate gauge transformations, the field equations can be put in the following form:

$$\Box^2 \left(h_{\mu\nu} - \tfrac{1}{2} h \eta_{\mu\nu} \right) = 2\kappa T_{\mu\nu} \, , \tag{6.8.7}$$

with

$$h_{,\nu}^{\mu\nu} = 0 \, . \tag{6.8.8}$$

We are supposing that the space coordinates are isotropic, so that:

$$h_{11} = h_{22} = h_{33} = h_s \, . \tag{6.8.9}$$

Furthermore, we suppose that the matter source is slow-moving and constituted by low density matter with a dust equation of state: $p = 0$. In this case, the perfect fluid energy-momentum tensor is represented by:

$$T^{\mu\nu} = \rho u^\mu u^\nu \, , \tag{6.8.10}$$

where, u^μ is the quadri-velocity and ρ represents the matter density. The perturbation is considered in its lower order.

With these considerations, we now may tackle the derivation of Lense-Thirring metric, in next Section.

We shall derive Lense-Thirring metric by two different lines of argument. The first will be by means of linearized General Relativity, as outlined here. The other is a transformation argument apparently first presented in Adler and Silbergleit (2000).

Referring to the linearized field equations derived above, namely:

$$\Box^2 \left(h_{\mu\nu} - \tfrac{1}{2} h \eta_{\mu\nu} \right) = 2\kappa T_{\mu\nu} \, , \tag{6.8.11}$$

and the gauge condition stated earlier:

$$h^{\mu\nu}_{,\nu} = 0 \,, \tag{6.8.12}$$

which is the analog of the same condition in electromagnetism, we have:

$$h_{00} = h_s = 2\Phi \,. \tag{6.8.13}$$

In Schwarzschild's metric we would have:

$$\Phi_{schw} = -\frac{GM}{2r} \,. \tag{6.8.14}$$

However, here the field equations are different:

$$\Box^2\Phi = -\kappa\rho \,, \tag{6.8.15}$$

$$\Box^2\vec{h} = 2\kappa\rho\vec{v} \,, \tag{6.8.16}$$

where $\vec{h} \equiv (h_{01}, h_{02}, h_{03})$ and $\vec{v}$ represents the source velocity. (In the same token, we shall obtain a different metric than Schwarzschild's).

We know from electromagnetism, how to solve (6.8.15) and (6.8.16) by means of re-tarded time potentials. The equation (6.8.15) yields a scalar function $\Phi(\vec{r}, t)$ which is called gravitoelectric potential. The second equation, (6.8.16), yields a new phenomenon called gravitomagnetism, represented by the gravitomagnetic vector potential $\vec{h}(\vec{r}, t)$.

When the system is nearly time-independent, the retarded time effect can be neglected, and we find a Newtonian potential (gravitoelectric-field) and a relativistic vector potential (gravitomagnetic field):

$$\Phi(\vec{r}) = -G \int \frac{\rho(\vec{r}')}{|\vec{r} - \vec{r}'|} d^3\vec{r}' \,, \tag{6.8.17}$$

and,

$$\vec{h}(\vec{r}) = 4G \int \frac{\rho(\vec{r}')\,\vec{v}(\vec{r}')}{|\vec{r} - \vec{r}'|} d^3\vec{r}' \,. \tag{6.8.18}$$

We have, thus, obtained the metric ("Lense-Thirring"):

$$ds^2 = (1 + 2\,\Phi)dt^2 - (1 - 2\,\Phi)d\vec{r}^2 + 2\vec{h}\cdot d\vec{r}\,dt \,. \tag{6.8.19}$$

The last term in r.h.s., accounts for gyroscope precessions ("Lense-Thirring effect").

Alternative derivation for the Lense-Thirring metric

We now shall consider the isotropic Schwarzschild's solution (Adler et al., 1975):

$$ds^2 = \frac{\left[1 - \frac{m}{2r}\right]^2}{\left[1 + \frac{m}{2r}\right]^2} dt^2 - \left[1 - \frac{m}{2r}\right]^4 d\vec{r}^2 \,, \tag{6.8.20}$$

Chapter 7

Properties of Black Holes

7.1. Radial Motion in Schwarzschild's Metric

For non-radial motion, i.e., for orbits around static spherically symmetric black holes, we refer to Chapter 5 in Part II. We now take care of radial motions.

We saw in Part II, that proper time, being measured by:

$$d\tau^2 = \frac{ds^2}{c^2},$$

assumes an extrema between two points, when traversed by an observer. It has been also introduced, in Part II, the association of the scalar equation $ds^2 = 0$, (which represented the path of light in Special Relativity), to describe null geodesics in GRT.

Consider radial inward fall towards a black hole. In matter exterior, we have $G_{\mu\nu} = 0$. So that, for a radius $r > R_S = 2GM$, we may write,

$$d\tau^2 = \frac{1}{\alpha}\left(dr^2 - \alpha^2 dt^2\right), \tag{7.1.1}$$

where,

$$\alpha = \frac{2GM}{r} - 1. \tag{7.1.2}$$

This is Schwarzschild's metric:
$$d\tau^2 > 0. \tag{7.1.3}$$

We shall have one of the two conditions below:

1st Condition: $\frac{dr}{dt} > \alpha.$ \hfill (7.1.3a)

2nd Condition: $\frac{dr}{dt} < -\alpha.$ \hfill (7.1.3b)

We conclude that, in the exterior, it is possible infall or outfall.

In radial motion, with $ds^2 < 0$, we obtain:

$$\frac{dr}{du} < \tfrac{1}{2}v.$$

(7.1.21)

While, in the interior case,

$$v = r - 2m < 0,$$

(7.1.22)

we would have the normal attractive motion,

$$\frac{dr}{du} < 0 .$$

(7.1.23)

In the case of (7.1.23) , we are in face of a *black hole*.

Outward motion, can be studied by changing the sign of the u - coordinate. Thus,

$$\frac{dr}{du} > 0 ,$$

(7.1.24)

and we find, a *white hole*.

It does not seem that there is any singularity when $r = 2m$.

We could as well study the path of null geodesics, i.e., $ds = 0$. No surprises will arise.

In summary:

1) in Schwarzschild's coordinates, outside the event horizon ($r = R_S = 2m$), an interior singularity, inside a matter distribution, is of no consequence, because the field equations employed in order to derive that metric (Schwarzschild's), are those in vacuum.

Then, when matter extravasates Schwarzschild's radius   ($r > R_S$), there is nothing new.

2) from relations   (7.1.3a) and (7.1.3b) , we know that for $r > R_S$, in the exterior, a state of motion is unavoidable. An infinitely far observer, finds that inward motion takes an infinite time, in order to reach the event horizon surface.

3) proper time, in the above case, is finite: a freely falling observer, inside the event horizon surface, will reach unavoidably the point $r = 0$.

4) outside the event horizon, both infall or outfall can be possible.

5) for motions across the surface of the event horizon, the singularity is of no consequence, and we replace the Schwarzschild's coordinates, by the metric (7.1.16).

6) in the new metric, in infall and outfall are not symmetric; no light or particle can

escape from the interior to the exterior of the event horizon surface, but the opposite flow is possible.

7) the new metric, when the time coordinate $u \to -u$, describes a new physical situation, with a reversed dynamics: this is a *white hole* .

8) we may talk of *white holes*, as "sources", while *black holes* could be described as "sinks" .

7.2. Frame-Dragging

In Lense-Thirring metric, we can find the "frame-dragging" effect, due to the fact that an observer at "rest", relative to a rotating source, finds a difference between his local inertial frame, and the "Machian" fixed stars frame, in a Lorentzian at infinity coordinate system.

Consider the isotropic form of L.T. metric,

$$ds^2 = \left(1 - \tfrac{2m}{r}\right) dt^2 - \left(1 + \tfrac{2m}{r}\right) d\sigma^2 + \tfrac{4J}{r} \sin^2\theta \, d\phi \, dt, \tag{7.2.1}$$

where,

$$r = \sqrt{x^2 + y^2 + z^2} \, . \tag{7.2.2}$$

Though a little tedious, we may find the geodesic equations for this metric, imposing also that the orbits are equatorial ($\theta = \tfrac{\pi}{2}$), while the rotation parameter a , and the relativistic mass m , are relatively small, $\left(\tfrac{a}{\rho}\right)^2 << 1$ and $\left(\tfrac{m}{\rho}\right)^2 << 1$, where now ρ stands for the radial coordinate :

$$\tfrac{d}{ds}\left[\rho^2\dot\phi + \tfrac{2ma}{\rho}\dot t\right] = 0. \tag{7.2.3}$$

$$\tfrac{d}{ds}\left[g_{00}\dot t - \tfrac{2ma}{\rho}\dot\phi\right] = 0. \tag{7.2.4}$$

In the above equations, overdots signify derivatives in the arc-length s . From the metric, we also find:

$$1 = g_{00}\dot t^2 - g_{00}^{-1}\dot\rho^2 - \rho^2\left[\dot\theta^2 + \dot\phi^2\sin^2\theta\right] - \tfrac{4ma}{\rho}\dot t\dot\phi\sin^2\theta \, . \tag{7.2.5}$$

The radial motion begins at $t = 0$ and $\phi = 0$. From (7.2.3), it follows that:

$$\rho^2\ddot\phi + 2ma\tfrac{d}{ds}\left(\tfrac{\dot t}{\rho}\right) = 0 \, ,$$

or,

$$\rho^2\ddot\phi + \tfrac{2ma}{\rho^2}\ddot t - \tfrac{2ma}{\rho^3}\dot t\dot\rho = 0. \tag{7.2.6}$$

From (7.2.4) and (7.2.5) we would have with,

$$l = g_{00}\dot t \, ,$$

In the above, the case $g_{00} = 0$, responds for the *static limit* , where $r = R_S$ (Schwarzschild's radius); this is only valid for the equatorial plane.   The temporal metric coefficient g_{00} in this case independs on the rotational parameter.

We define the *ergosphere* , by the condition,

$$R_S > r > R_H .$$ (7.3.12)

In this zone, *frame-dragging* can not be overruled in anyway: the "fixed" stars would be not so, for an observer located in the ergosphere.

Consider the path of light, $ds = 0$, from an initial condition where the light is along the ϕ - direction, in the static equatorial limit, where $dr = 0$: this defines an initial tangential motion.

The temporal metric coefficient is given by,

$$g_{00} = R^2 \dot{\phi}^2 - \frac{4M^2}{r} \dot{\phi}.$$ (7.3.13)

We have here clearly an angular velocity given by,

$$\omega = \dot{\phi} = \frac{d\phi}{dt} .$$ (7.3.14)

Then, it follows that,

$$\omega = \frac{2M^2}{rR^2} \pm \frac{2M^2}{rR^2} \left[1 + \frac{r^2 R^2}{4M^4} g_{00} \right]^{1/2} .$$ (7.3.15)

In the static limit, we would have, along with $r = R_S$,

$$R^2 = R_S^2 = 6M^2 .$$ (7.3.16)

We find, for ω (see relation 7.3.15), two different solutions, namely,

$$\omega_1 = 0,$$ (7.3.17)

and,

$$\omega_2 = \frac{4M^2}{r_s R_S^2} = \frac{1}{3M}.$$ (7.3.18)

Suppose that the light ray would be send in the direction of rotation (of the black hole); then, ω
would be given, at $t = 0$, by the second solution, i.e., $\omega = \omega_2$. Now, for the

opposite direction, it can be checked that, due to the anticipated frame-dragging effect, counter rotation motion is forbidden.

For a massive particle, (i.e., following a temporal world line), we would have,

$$ds^2 > 0, \quad (\text{at } r = R_S).$$

In the same extreme Kerr black hole, again in the equatorial plane, initial tangential motion, mean $a = M$, and $dr = 0$ (at $t = 0$). Then, we would have,

$$g_{00} = 1 - \frac{2M}{R_S} = 0. \tag{7.3.19}$$

Then,

$$ds^2 = \frac{4M^2}{2M} d\phi dt - R^2 d\phi^2. \tag{7.3.20}$$

But we also find,

$$R^2 = R_S^2 + M^2 + 2M^3/R_S = 6M^2. \tag{7.3.21}$$

From (7.3.20) and (7.3.21),

$$ds^2 = \left[2\omega - 6M^2\omega^2 \right] dt^2 > 0 \tag{7.3.22}$$

The above implies that,

$$\frac{1}{6M^2} > \omega > 0. \tag{7.3.23}$$

Evidently, at the initial instant, there is a forward dragging.

The above particular situations, represent a general effect, which was also evident from the Lense-Thirring metric.

Locally non-rotating observer

It is also possible to find, within a Kerr black hole, a locally non-rotating observer, as follows. Let us write the Kerr's metric as:

$$ds^2 = \left[g_{00} - \frac{g_{\phi t}^2}{g_{\phi\phi}} \right] dt^2 + g_{\phi\phi} \left[d\phi + \frac{g_{\phi t}}{g_{\phi\phi}} dt \right]^2 + g_{\theta\theta} d\theta^2 + g_{rr} dr^2. \tag{7.3.24}$$

It is not surprising that we may, from the above, identify an angular speed $\omega = \dot{\phi}$, for a far-away observer; if we impose that, for a local observer,

$$\omega = \dot{\phi} = \frac{d\phi}{dt} = -\frac{g_{\phi t}}{g_{\phi\phi}}, \tag{7.3.25}$$

the metric will become "non-rotating", along his world line:

$$ds^2 = \left[g_{00} - \frac{g_{\phi t}^2}{g_{\phi\phi}} \right] dt^2 + g_{\theta\theta} d\theta^2 + g_{rr} dr^2. \tag{7.3.26}$$

There is a distinction to be made: a zero angular speed, does not imply that the particle will have zero angular momentum, and vice-versa. For instance, consider radial infall, from rest at infinity. If the initial angular momentum along the rotation axis, is null, by conservation law, it will still be zero during the fall. However, this same particle, can acquire an angular speed.

We now drop the bar from the time coordinate. And, we indeed proved Birkhoff's theorem!!!

The equivalent result for electrodynamics, in Special Relativity, tells us that a spherically symmetric solution of Maxwell's equations is by all means, static. There is no difference, in GRT, between the exterior metric, of a static mass distribution, or a pulsating one, if spherical symmetry is kept.

We recall that a stationary metric has time independent metric coefficients. A diagonal metric, then, is static. This was not evident from Schwarzschild' solution, because we had imposed static conditions, beforehand, and asymptotic flatness; however, by a more accurate analysis, we could have derived this for any spherically symmetric metric, which obeyed Einstein's field equations. Even if the source would not be static, the exterior solution would not be changed. No gravitational waves could than, possibly, be generated outside the event horizon surface; from the interior, of course, no signals could also find their way to the outside.

Removable singularities

We have already shown, that the singularity at $r = 0$, is "real", or "intrinsic", or "essential". Such singularities, are defined by the condition that a change in the coordinate system can not get rid of them. Not so, for the Schwarzschild's black hole, is the surface at $r = R_S$:

$$\lim_{r \to R_S} g_{rr} \to \infty .$$

We saw earlier, that this was a kind of "removable" singularity: a coordinate transformation did the job. In any case, if we calculated the Ricci scalar, at that point, we would find no singular result. However, for $r = 0$, the Ricci scalar would be given by,

$$R \equiv R_{\alpha\beta\gamma\delta} R^{\alpha\beta\gamma\delta} = \frac{48}{r^6} M^2 ,$$

(do not confuse R as define in Chapter 2, with the same one symbol of last Section), so that,

$$\lim_{r \to 0} R \to \infty .$$

For a charged rotating black hole (Kerr-Newman) , the non-removable singularities, could only be explained, likewise in the Schwarzschild's case by the argument that GRT field equations would be invalid, either for extremely intensive gravitational fields or for microphysical events, when Quantum effects would play a rôle. Though, in this place, we do not study gravitational collapse, we argue in the last Chapter of this book, that collapse towards $r = 0$ could be halted by anti-gravitational forces which surge inside KN black holes, generating a finite minimum non-zero radius. (Berman, 2006). Quantum gravity theories, *albeit* provisional, yield similar conclusions.

"No-hair" theorem

John Archibald Wheeler, one of the greatest physicists of all times, who had no prejudice against bald persons, coined a theorem as "no-hair" — , by the statement that if you meet one black hole, the only properties that define it, are its total, mass (M), electric charge (Q), magnetic charge (P) and angular momentum (J). This means that all such beings are indistinguishable, if they have the same above said properties, as he was unable to distinguish any two bald persons.

Uniqueness and Israel theorems

As Birkhoff's theorem states that a spherically symmetric vacuum solution must be static in the exterior, there is also a uniqueness theorem under which Schwarzschild's metric is the unique spherical and symmetrical solution in vacuum, which can obey Einstein's field equations.

The converse, named Israel's theorem, states that, provided that a vacuum field is static, it must be spherical, and thus, it can be represented as a Schwarzschild's exterior field.

From the above, it results that, within GRT, we have:

(i). Schwarzschild's metric is the only static vacuum solution.

(ii). in the same case as in (i), any other solution that could possibly be presented, will result in the Schwarzschild's metric by a convenient coordinate transformation;

Accretion, trapping, and membranes

In a non-vacuum exterior, something as a black hole, presents an infinite red-shift surface, defined by a null value for the temporal metric coefficient , i.e., $g_{00} = 0$. Of course, the zero value is not valid at all points, but only for a particular set of coordinates, which define such "surface". To an external observer, as stated, this is an infinite red-shift surface which may not coincide with the event horizon.

A flash of light emitted from a surface, moving normal to this surface outside a black hole make inward rays define decreasing wavefront areas, while the outward rays have increasing surface wavefronts. The inward normals of the surfaces, i.e., the inward normals to the inward wavefronts, must converge; the outward normals, to the outward wavefronts, should diverge.

In both cases, in the interior of the black hole, as the center of attraction lies at $r = 0$ we find convergences; the emitting surfaces, is thus called "trapped".

The "true" event horizon, has a defining global property in geometrical terms: it describes the limit among those null geodesics, that reach infinity, from those which do not. The apparent horizon, is the outermost trapped surface; it is a local construct, because you can test it for local convergence or divergence of the null rays.

we infer that it is not the area $4\pi R_S^2$ which defines the entropy, but relation (8.1.1), which means that what matters is $V_S^{1/2}$, where V_S stands for the Schwarzschild's event horizon volume.

The final black hole mass, M'_{bh}, which results from the coalescence, of the two $\frac{1}{2}M_{bh}$ black holes, makes the initial and final entropies to become:

$$S_i = 2KR_S^{3/2} = 2KM_{bh}^{3/2}, \tag{8.1.2}$$

and,

$$S_f = K\left(2M'^{3/2}\right) = 2\sqrt{2}KM'^{3/2}. \tag{8.1.3}$$

If the total mass is constant, i.e.,

$$M'_{bh} = \sum_i M_i = M_{bh}, \tag{8.1.4}$$

we find that, because of the accretion, the entropy has increased:

$$S_f > \sum_i S_i. \tag{8.1.5}$$

Thus, the entropy is always increasing, or at least, constant. It is the square root of the Schwarzschild's volume that represents the increased entropy in the above example.

For an isolated black hole, when there is no absorption of more mass-energy from the neighborhood, the entropy is constant. In other words, when there is no more accretion,

$$\dot{R}_S = 2\dot{M}_S = 0. \tag{8.1.6}$$

This is different from what happens with the Universe, for it is expanding, i.e.,

$$\dot{R}_U > 0. \tag{8.1.7}$$

So, the entropy of the Universe, S_U, also grows with time:

$$\dot{S}_U > 0. \tag{8.1.8}$$

In "local" Physics, the entropy of a black hole, is constant. Of course, the black hole is part of the Universe, but this is "global" Physics.

8.2. Loss of Information Paradox

The so-called loss of information paradox, is due to disinformation of some physicists. As we have seen in last Section, an isolated black hole, has constant entropy. The information contents is preserved. In case of accretion from the neighborhood, there is a mass increase, inside the black hole, which causes locally a growth of entropy,

$$\Delta S_{bh} > 0 \, . \tag{8.2.1}$$

But in the outside, there is another physical system that lost local mass, an for that system, we have,

$$\Delta S_{exterior} < 0 \, . \tag{8.2.2}$$

The total local entropy variation is zero, i.e., the black hole gains entropy, but the exterior looses it,

$$\sum_i \Delta S = \Delta S_{bh} + \Delta S_{exterior} = 0. \tag{8.2.3}$$

So, entropy remains locally constant. In the absence of accretion, it is the black hole by itself, that remains with constant entropy.

It has been argued that, due to the absolute temperature assigned to a black hole, there is evaporation, which causes entropy variation. However, this would be a Quantum Mechanical phenomenon, while here we deal with Classical Physics, like GRT. The assignment of a temperature, was done by us on a Classical Thermodynamical framework. Indeed, the radiational energy density formula,

$$\rho = \sigma T^4 \, , \qquad (\sigma = \text{constant}) \tag{8.2.4}$$

which, by comparison with the energy density of a Schwarzschild's black hole, (Part IV, Chapter 10), derived as,

$$\rho = \beta R_S^{-2} \, , \qquad (\beta = \text{constant}) \tag{8.2.5}$$

gave rise to the relation ,

$$R_S T_{bh}^2 = \text{constant} \, ,$$

may be obtained through Classical Thermodynamics (Sears and Salinger, 1975), where the constant σ is undetermined. Any evaporation concept, depends on the radiational power output, which depends on $R_S T_{bh}^2$, and is thus constant. For the power formula, consult Halliday et al., (2005). Because this formula depends on Planck's constant, which is extraneous to Classical Physics, it can not be applied. Besides, the idea of T_{bh} characterization, is purely formal; no one may think of this temperature as "real".

Would there be a Cosmological evaporation of the Universe? This can not happen, for any heat flow needs a gradient of temperature, but the Universe can not have a temperature gradient with anything else.

Summarizing: 1st) the entropy of the Universe grows, for the Universe expands. It is a global phenomenon; 2nd) the entropy of a black hole, is a local concept; it increases during accretion processes; but is constant for an isolated one; 3rd) if there is accretion, so that the black hole entropy increases locally, the neighborhood looses entropy, in the same value,

$$\frac{\ddot{R}}{R} = -\left[\frac{4\pi G}{3}\left(\rho + 3p - \frac{2\Lambda}{\kappa}\right) + \frac{2}{3}\sigma^2\right] + \left[\frac{2}{3}\omega^2 + \frac{1}{2}\dot{v}^{\mu}_{;\mu}\right] , \tag{8.3.21}$$

where σ , ω and $\dot{v}^{\mu}_{;\mu}$ describe respectively shear, vorticity, and acceleration; the last one, is the responsible for driving the system out of geodesic motion, which derives from non-acceleration. It can be seen that the first bracket in the rhs, causes gravitational attraction, unless the cosmological constant Λ is very large and positive. The second bracket describes repulsive gravitational terms, i.e., vorticities and accelerations. If the first bracket terms would prevail, with small Λ , gravitational attraction will make R decrease, towards a singularity, when $R = 0$.

It will be shown in Part IV, Section 10.4, that there is a surge of anti-gravitational phenomena, when, by gravitational collapse, a black hole has negative energy. As the Universe is a kind of black hole, in Section 14.1, we describe how the Universe, and possibly, a gravitational collapse, does not end in a singular point, with zero volume; before such possible event, anti-gravitational forces, turn contraction into expansion. In Raychaudhuri's equation, it means that the constant G changes from a positive to a negative value; the first bracket in the rhs becomes repulsive.

On the other hand, there is a limit in GRT, because it is a Classical theory, and for small radii, lesser than Planck's length, the theory could not possibly work; Quantum phenomena enter the scenario. There are Heisenberg's uncertainties, and there is no use in talking classically on a zero radius.

For black holes, there are some kinds of singularities that are not "intrinsic", or "essential": we encountered them in Section 7.1. For instance, a fortuitous null value for g_{00} ; by a change in coordinates, we showed that the problem was mathematical, i.e., coordinate system dependent, and not a Physics problem. In this way, the initial singularity of Cosmology, or the null value of g_{00} , for a point, in black hole description, which made $g_{rr} \to \infty$, are not worrisome, as we have commented above.

From Section 7.1, we found that a radial free-fall, from a far-away zone, where there is an infinitely far observer, makes a slowing-down of the free-falling coordinate time; when $r = R_S$, time is frozen: the far-away observer measures an infinite time for the free-fall to reach the event horizon. Gravitational collapse of a star goes in a similar way. The far-away observer can not see inside the event horizon, but both the free-fall observer and the star radius, keep going through the "hole". At that point, free-fall is irresistible, and ends when $r = 0$. Believe it or not!!!

It turns out that the event horizon clothes the collapse from distant observers. There is a Cosmic Censorship that prevents the distant observer from observing the collapse inside the surface defined by $r = R_S$. If it were not so, we would have a naked singularity (Penrose, 1969). According to Penrose (1979), no singularity is observable, with the exception of the initial instant of the Universe's singularity. However, we have discussed above this case. The Cosmic Censorship hypothesis, is the statement of the inexistence of naked singularities. Only singularities hidden by event horizons would be in existence.

For more, go to Section 8.5.

8.4. The Universe as a White-Hole

The Journal *Astrophysics and Space Science*, will publish soon a paper with the contents of this Section. This is based on a method published by Gomide and Berman(1988; first edition in 1986); we believe that the present calculation has not been published by someone else.

Pathria(1972) published a paper showing that, for certain values of the cosmological constant, a pressureless finite (positively curved) Universe could be inside a white-hole, if it obeyed Robertson-Walker's metric (with $k = 1$):

$$ds^2 = dt^2 - \frac{R^2(t)}{\left[1+\left(\frac{kr^2}{4}\right)\right]^2}d\sigma^2 , \tag{8.4.1}$$

where,

$$d\sigma^2 = dx^2 + dy^2 + dz^2 . \tag{8.4.2}$$

If R stands for the radius of a "large sphere" of mass M, while G stands for Newton's gravitational constant, a white-hole could be described by the condition that R is smaller than its Schwarzschild's radius:

$$R < 2GM. \tag{8.4.3}$$

It is known, on experimental grounds, that the present Universe, obeys the Machian relation by Brans and Dicke(1961),

$$R \sim GM. \tag{8.4.4}$$

We, thus, can think that the Universe may be inside a white-hole, but this should be analyzed by means of Einstein's field equations for the above metric,

$$\kappa\rho = 3H^2 + \frac{3k}{R^2} + \Lambda , \tag{8.4.5}$$

$$\kappa p = -2\frac{\ddot{R}}{R} - H^2 - \frac{k}{R^2} - \Lambda, \tag{8.4.6}$$

where,

$$H = \frac{\dot{R}}{R} ,$$

and,

$$\kappa = 8\pi G.$$

We study below, all three tricurvature cases ($k = 0, \pm 1$). We also treat the absolute temperature of black holes and the Universe.

Conclusions

We have shown, in a different context than in Pathria's paper (where $p = 0$, and Λ obeys certain conditions), that the closed Robertson-Walker's Universe, with any value of p constrained to obey Einstein's field equations may be thought as being a white-hole. Brans-Dicke relation to the problem is not conclusive, because it represents only a Machian condition for the Universe. In a similar way, flat or open Universes, in the expanding phase, may become white-holes after R becoming larger than $\sqrt{\frac{3}{\Lambda}}$. The Machian condition for the Universe, was taken, partially, as implying that the absolute temperature ran like $\left(\sqrt{R} \right)^{-1}$. (Section 8.1 and Part V, Section 12.7). The standard condition, however, is that $T \propto R^{-1}$.

8.5. More on Black Holes

We refer the reader to a Chapter written by Mario Rabinowitz (Rabinowitz, 2006; Kreitler, 2006b), on Black Hole Paradoxes.

In the first place, we show how he presents Winterberg's simple derivation of Schwarzschild's metric (Chapter 6).

By conservation of energy, a body of mass m attains velocity v, when falling from rest, into a central gravitational field of mass M, given by:

$$\tfrac{1}{2}v^2 - \tfrac{GM}{r} = 0 \, . \tag{8.5.1}$$

From Special Relativity, there is a length contraction when a body acquires a speed v, given by:

$$dr = dr' \sqrt{1 - v^2/c^2} \, , \tag{8.5.2}$$

and a time dilation,

$$dt = \frac{dt'}{\sqrt{1 - v^2/c^2}} \, . \tag{8.5.3}$$

On combining (8.5.1) with (8.5.2) and (8.5.3), we obtain new relations,

$$dr = dr' \sqrt{1 - v^2/c^2} = dr' \sqrt{1 - 2GM/(c^2 r)} \, , \tag{8.5.4}$$

and,

$$dt = \frac{dt'}{\sqrt{1 - v^2/c^2}} = \frac{dt'}{\sqrt{1 - 2GM/(c^2 r)}} \, . \tag{8.5.5}$$

The idea is that a far-away observer (at $r \to \infty$), measures length and time intervals, getting as a result, dr and dt. The local observer, measures dr' and dt'; the local observer, is the observer in the rest frame of the body which free-falls.

Consider now the spherical coordinates form of the line element of Special Relativistic Minkowski's spacetime:

$$ds^2 = c^2 dt^2 - dr^2 - r^2 d\Omega , \qquad (8.5.6)$$

and,

$$ds'^2 = c^2 dt'^2 - dr'^2 - r'^2 d\Omega'. \qquad (8.5.7)$$

The metric is invariant, $ds^2 = ds'^2$. For radial infall, $d\theta = d\phi = 0$. We have no reason to decide against $d\theta' = d\phi' = 0$, for the same reason. Now, we make use of (8.5.4) and (8.5.5), plugging into (8.5.7), in order to find,

$$ds^2 = c^2 \left[1 - 2GM/\left(c^2 r\right)\right] dt^2 - \left[1 - 2GM/\left(c^2 r\right)\right]^{-1} dr^2. \qquad (8.5.8)$$

When, the angular variables are not constant, we add, to (8.5.8), the term $r^2 d\Omega$. So that, Schwarzschild's metric, has been found, namely,

$$ds^2 = c^2 \left[1 - 2GM/\left(c^2 r\right)\right] dt^2 - \left[1 - 2GM/\left(c^2 r\right)\right]^{-1} dr^2 + r^2 d\Omega. \qquad (8.5.9)$$

Having found the metric, Rabinowitz has been careful to observe that black holes collapse is unobservable. In fact, he reasons that Schwarzschild's radius, which defines the event horizon, is given by:

$$R_S = \frac{2GM}{c^2} . \qquad (8.5.10)$$

For $r = R_S$, equation (8.5.1) shows that $v = c =$ relativistic limit. A distant observer watches that the time coordinate begins to slow down during free-fall, until time becomes "frozen", at that point, where $r = R_S$. The time interval, for the total free-fall towards that radius, is infinite, from the far-away observer's point of view. It would be just the same for the collapse of an astrophysical object, subject to the gravitational field alone. For such object, it may well be that it keeps collapsing until $r \to 0$; however, no one in the exterior, will even see the object when it undergoes the passage from $r > R_S$, towards $r = R_S$. As Rabinowitz points out, the collapse into a black hole is unobservable, and also unstoppable, after its starts, by current orthodoxy parameters. From equation relating dt and dt', we see that, for $v \to c$, the time interval goes to infinity, or, we may say that the light from the body acquires an infinite value for its wavelength. Any radiation emitted from the free-falling observer, or from more interior regions, suffer from the gravitational red-shift and any particle escaping from the center, but beginning its escape within the $r > R_S$ spherical zone, must loose energy (see Section 7.1).

Penrose (1969) presented his cosmic censorship conjecture, under which distant observers can not see naked singularities; in 1979, Penrose states that no singularity, except the big-bang, could ever be "seen" by any observer. First of all, if there is a singularity in the scenario, the field equations break down: it has never been asserted by any one who does

Chapter 9

Variational Methods in General Relativity

9.1. Variational calculus and Special Relativity

Consider a physical system described by an "action" integral,

$$I = \int L\left(q, q_{,\mu}\right) d^3x\, dt = \int L\, d^4x, \qquad (9.1.1)$$

where, L is a Lagrangian density, and q is a "state" quantity, i.e., it defines the state of the system. The integral I is called the Lagrangian of the system. The action principle, is defined by,

$$\delta I = 0. \qquad (9.1.2)$$

The variation symbol δ defines variations among two possible "trajectories" relative to the effective or real one, which makes (9.1.2) valid, provided that, in the initial and the final positions (to be referred to, A and B) the displacements $\delta q(A) = \delta q(B) = 0$. (For more details, the reader should consult a book on variational techniques; we suggest, Lovelock and Rund, 1975).

From (9.1.1) and (9.1.2), we may write,

$$\delta I = \int_A^B \left[\frac{\partial L}{\partial q}\delta q + \frac{\partial L}{\partial q_{,\mu}}\delta q_{,\mu}\right] d^4x =$$

$$= \int_A^B \left\{\frac{\partial L}{\partial q}\delta q + \left[\left(\frac{\partial L}{\partial q_{,\mu}}\right)\delta q\right]_{,\mu} - \left[\frac{\partial L}{\partial q_{,\mu}}\right]_{,\mu}\delta q\right\} d^4x = 0. \qquad (9.1.3)$$

We know from Gauss theorem, that,

$$\int_A^B \left[\left(\frac{\partial L}{\partial q_{,\mu}}\right)\delta q\right]_{,\mu} d^4x = \oint \frac{\partial L}{\partial q_{,\mu}}\delta q\, dS = 0. \qquad (9.1.4)$$

In order to find the correct form of $T^{\mu\nu}$, despite the apparent "freedom", we demand that, when defining an angular momentum tensor $M^{\gamma\alpha\beta}$, from $T^{\mu\nu}$, the symmetry in $T^{\mu\nu}$ indices, imply the conservation law,

$$M^{\gamma\alpha\beta}{}_{,\gamma} = \left[x^\alpha T^{\beta\gamma} - x^\beta T^{\alpha\gamma}\right]_{,\gamma} = 0. \tag{9.1.15}$$

The usual angular momentum space components J^{23}, J^{31} and J^{12}, referring respectively to the coordinate axes x^1, x^2 and x^3 are determined by,

$$J^{\alpha\beta} = -J^{\beta\alpha} = \int M^{0\alpha\beta} d^3x. \tag{9.1.16}$$

The space-time components J^{0i} (with $i = 1, 2, 3$) can be made to disappear by a proper choice of the coordinate system.

We now have to show, that our definition for angular momentum leads to a conservation law. From (9.1.15) and (9.1.16), we have, from Gauss theorem,

$$J^{\alpha\beta}{}_{,\beta} = \frac{\partial}{\partial x^\beta} \int \left[x^\alpha T^{\beta 0} - x^\beta T^{\alpha 0}\right] d^3x = \int \left[\delta^\alpha_\beta T^{\beta 0} - T^{\alpha 0}\right] d^3x + \int \left[T^{\beta 0} - T^{\alpha 0}\right] dS . \tag{9.1.17}$$

We find that only for a symmetric $T^{\mu\nu}$, we shall have a conservation law, i.e.,

$$J^{\alpha\beta}{}_{,\beta} = 0 .$$

We remind the reader, that we began this Section, by defining a single state quantity, q. In fact, we could have proceeded all along, by a real energy momentum tensor defined by several state quantities q_ν. Then, we would replace (9.1.13) by the following:

$$T^\beta_\alpha = \sum_\nu \left[q_{\nu,\alpha} \frac{\partial \mathcal{L}}{\partial q_{\nu,\beta}}\right] - \delta^\beta_\alpha \mathcal{L} \tag{9.1.18}$$

We could also extend our range of options, and make, as state variables, the metric tensor components, something that is done in General Relativity.

9.2.   Variational Derivation of the Field Equations

There is no way of deriving the Einstein's field equations from first principles. Neither would this be possible from variational principles unless one guessed before, what is being done.

We refer to Bergmann(1942), for the treatment given below. The only scalar that yields second order field equations, is the Ricci scalar R, for the variational principle, $\delta I = 0$, where,

$$I = \int_A^B R\sqrt{-g}d^4x \, . \tag{9.2.1}$$

The endpoint conditions, like in the last Section, are,

$$\delta g_{\mu\nu}(A) = \delta g_{\mu\nu}(B) = 0 \, , \tag{9.2.2}$$

and,

$$\delta g_{\mu\nu,\alpha}(A) = \delta g_{\mu\nu,\alpha}(B) = 0 \, . \tag{9.2.3}$$

Again, for intermediate point, the above variations $\delta g_{\mu\nu}$ and $\delta g_{\mu\nu,\alpha}$ are totally arbitrary.

[We recall that, in Section 2.5, which, according to the Preface, could be skipped, and if the reader did so, then, he should also do the same with the present Section; however, in Section 9.4, he will find hints on tensor densities, when employed in the variational energy problem.].

Let us call,

$$\bar{R} = \sqrt{-g}R \, . \tag{9.2.4}$$

From the definition above, $\bar{R}$ is a scalar density, so that, in transforming from one coordinate system to another, say, $x \rightarrow x'$, we would have,

$$\bar{R}' = JR \, , \tag{9.2.5}$$

where J stands for the Jacobian determinant,

$$J = \det\left[\frac{\partial x^\alpha}{\partial x'^\beta}\right]. \tag{9.2.6}$$

This guarantees that,

$$I' = I = \text{ invariant} \, . \tag{9.2.7}$$

Writing in full,

$$I' = \int_A^B \bar{R}'d^4x' = \int_A^B RJd^4x' = I \, . \tag{9.2.8}$$

The invariance of I , implies that the consequent Euler-Langrange equations, independs on the particular coordinate system in use; they are covariant differential equations.

We recall now the definition of the Ricci-scalar, in terms of the connections, so that,

and,

$$\bar{T}_\rho^\nu = \sqrt{-g}\, T_\rho^\nu \,. \tag{9.3.4a}$$

The field equations read now:

$$\sqrt{-g}\,[G_{\mu\nu}] = -\kappa \bar{T}_{\mu\nu} \,, \tag{9.3.4b}$$

where, $G_{\mu\nu}$ stands for Einstein's tensor.

Then, if:

$$\lim_{r \to \infty} \left[\bar{T}_\lambda^\nu + t_\lambda^\nu\right] = 0, \tag{9.3.5}$$

where r is the radial coordinate, then we may write that:

$$P_\lambda = \int \left[\bar{T}_\lambda^0 + t_\lambda^0\right]\, d^3x = \text{constants}\,. \tag{9.3.6}$$

In other words: the energy-momentum-pseudoquadrivector has constant components. This is the generalization from Special Relativity.

Now, suppose we can find the "superpotential" $U_\lambda^{\mu\nu}$, such that:

$$\kappa \left[\bar{T}_\lambda^\nu + t_\lambda^\nu\right] = U_{\lambda,\sigma}^{\nu\sigma} \,, \tag{9.3.7}$$

Then,

$$P_\lambda = \tfrac{1}{\kappa} \left\{ \int U_{\lambda,i}^{0i} + U_{\lambda,0}^{00} \right\} d^3x = \text{constants}\,. \qquad (i = 1,2,3) \tag{9.3.8a}$$

Suppose now that $U_\lambda^{\nu\sigma}$ is antisymmetric in the upper indices, i.e.,

$$U_\lambda^{\nu\sigma} = -U_\lambda^{\sigma\nu}. \tag{9.3.9}$$

The integral above (9.3.8a) then reduces to:

$$P_\lambda = \tfrac{1}{\kappa} \int U_{\lambda,i}^{0i}\, d^3x = \text{constant}\,. \qquad (i = 1,2,3) \tag{9.3.10}$$

In Special Relativity, of course, there is no room for a gravitational field, and $t^{\mu\nu} = 0$, so that:

$$P_\lambda = \int \bar{T}_\lambda^0\, d^3x = \text{constant}\,. \tag{9.3.11}$$

We claim and show in next Section, that:

$$U_\lambda^{\mu\nu} = \tfrac{1}{2\sqrt{-g}} g_{\lambda\alpha} \left[\bar{g}^{\mu\alpha}\bar{g}^{\nu\beta} - \bar{g}^{\nu\alpha}\bar{g}^{\mu\beta}\right]_{,\beta} \,. \tag{9.3.12}$$

The above $U_\lambda^{\mu\nu}$ is called Freud's or Einstein's superpotential.

We claim that, when we use the definition of the Christoffel symbols in terms of the metric tensor components, the superpotential would become:

$$U_\lambda^{\mu\nu} = \frac{1}{2\sqrt{-g}} g_{\lambda\alpha} \left[\bar{g}^{\mu\alpha}\bar{g}^{\nu\beta} - \bar{g}^{\nu\alpha}\bar{g}^{\mu\beta} \right]_{,\beta} + \frac{1}{2} \left[\delta_\lambda^\nu \bar{g}_{,\alpha}^{\mu\alpha} - \bar{g}_{,\lambda}^{\mu\nu} \right]. \tag{9.3.17}$$

However the last two terms in the r.h.s. do not contribute to the definition (9.3.7), so that we obtain relation (9.3.12); this is due to the identity,

$$\bar{g}_{,\alpha\lambda}^{\mu\alpha} - \bar{g}_{,\lambda\nu}^{\mu\lambda} \equiv \left[\delta_\lambda^\nu \bar{g}_{,\alpha}^{\mu\alpha} - \bar{g}_{,\lambda}^{\mu\nu} \right]_{,\nu} \equiv 0 . \tag{9.3.18}$$

From Einstein's superpotential, $U_\lambda^{\mu\nu}$, we can find other superpotentials and the corresponding pseudotensors, with their energy-momentum-pseudoquadrivectors.

By definition, we have:

$$U_{\lambda,\sigma}^{\rho\sigma} = \kappa \left[\bar{T}_\lambda^\rho + t_\lambda^\rho \right]. \tag{9.3.19}$$

On multiplying both sides of the above, by $\vec{g}^{\lambda\mu}$ we find:

$$\tilde{U}_{,\sigma}^{\mu\rho\sigma} = \kappa\sqrt{-g}\left[\bar{T}^{\mu\rho} + \tilde{t}^{\mu\rho} \right], \tag{9.3.20}$$

where, taking care of the identity:

$$\vec{g}^{\lambda\mu}U_{\lambda,\sigma}^{\rho\sigma} = \left(\vec{g}^{\lambda\mu}U_\lambda^{\rho\sigma} \right)_{,\sigma} - \vec{g}_{,\sigma}^{\lambda\mu}U_\lambda^{\rho\sigma} , \tag{9.3.20a}$$

we define a new pseudotensor $\tilde{t}^{\mu\rho}$ and a new superpotential $\tilde{U}^{\mu\rho\sigma}$ so that:

$$\kappa\sqrt{-g}\,\tilde{t}^{\mu\rho} \equiv \kappa\vec{g}^{\lambda\mu}t_\lambda^\rho + \vec{g}_{,\sigma}^{\lambda\mu}\,U_\lambda^{\rho\sigma}, \tag{9.3.21}$$

and,

$$\tilde{U}^{\mu\rho\sigma} \equiv \vec{g}^{\lambda\mu}U_\lambda^{\rho\sigma} = -\tilde{U}^{\mu\sigma\rho} . \tag{9.3.22}$$

The new superpotential $\tilde{U}^{\mu\rho\sigma}$ is called after Landau-Lifshitz. From Einstein's superpotential relation (9.3.12) we find now that:

$$\tilde{U}^{\mu\rho\sigma} = \frac{1}{2} \left[\bar{g}^{\rho\mu}\bar{g}^{\sigma\beta} - \bar{g}^{\sigma\mu}\bar{g}^{\rho\beta} \right]_{,\beta}. \tag{9.3.23}$$

From the above we rewrite (9.3.20) as:

$$\kappa\sqrt{-g}\left[\bar{T}^{\mu\rho} + \tilde{t}^{\mu\rho} \right] = \frac{1}{2} \left[\bar{g}^{\rho\mu}\bar{g}^{\sigma\beta} - \bar{g}^{\sigma\mu}\bar{g}^{\rho\beta} \right]_{,\beta\sigma}. \tag{9.3.24}$$

It follows that, as $\bar{T}^{\mu\rho}$ is symmetric, i.e.,

$$\bar{T}^{\mu\rho} = g^{\lambda\mu}\bar{T}_\lambda^\rho = \sqrt{-g}T^{\mu\rho} , \tag{9.3.24a}$$

$$g' = -\det g'_{\mu\nu} \, .$$

J is the Jacobian of the transformation $x' \to x$, denoted

$$J = \left| \frac{\partial x}{\partial x'} \right| = \det \left| \frac{\partial x^\rho}{\partial x'^\mu} \right| .$$

The determinant g is called a scalar density.

In the transformation $x \to x'$, the volume element in a four-dimensional space, transforms like:

$$d^4 x' = J^{-1} d^4 x \, .$$

An invariant volume element, should be expressed by:

$$\left[\sqrt{g} d^4 x \right] \to \left[\sqrt{g'} d^4 x' \right] .$$

We know that the covariant divergence of the energy momentum tensor, is given by:

$$T^{\mu\nu}_{;\nu} = \left[\sqrt{g} T^{\mu\nu} \right]_{;\nu} = 0 \, . \tag{9.4.1}$$

In the presence of a gravitational field, there might be found a pseudo-tensor $t^{\mu\nu}$ such that there could be a conservation law of the type

$$\left[\sqrt{g} T^{\mu\nu} + t^{\mu\nu} \right]_{,\nu} = 0. \tag{9.4.2}$$

In a geodesic reference system, the gravitational field representative ($t^{\mu\nu}$), should disappear: if we call with a bar, the geodesic system energy momentum quantities, we would find:

$$\left[\sqrt{g} \overline{T}^{\mu\nu} \right]_{,\nu} = 0. \tag{9.4.3}$$

The reason for keeping the coefficient $\sqrt{g}$ in the above equation, is that upon integration, we need an invariant volume.

Imagine a superpotential $U^{\rho\sigma}_\lambda$, such that, from relation (9.4.2), we obtained, in the general case:

$$\frac{\partial}{\partial x^\sigma} U^{\rho\sigma}_\lambda = U^{\rho\sigma}_{\lambda,\sigma} = \left[\sqrt{g} T^\rho_\lambda + t^\rho_\lambda \right]. \tag{9.4.4}$$

In the particular case of the geodesic system, we would obtain:

$$\frac{\partial}{\partial x^\sigma} \overline{U}^{\rho\sigma}_\lambda = \overline{U}^{\rho\sigma}_{\lambda,\sigma} = \sqrt{g} \overline{T}^\rho_\lambda . \tag{9.4.5}$$

From the field equations,

$$R^\mu_\nu - \tfrac{1}{2} \delta^\mu_\nu R = T^\mu_\nu , \qquad (\text{with } \kappa = 1) , \tag{9.4.6}$$

we may find the components, $\bar{T}_\nu^\mu$, in the geodesic system, by means of $\bar{R}_\nu^\mu$ and $\bar{R}$, while remembering that,

$$\bar{g}_{,\mu}^{\alpha\beta} = 0 . \tag{9.4.7}$$

Obviously, we also can write,

$$\bar{\Gamma}_{\beta\lambda}^\alpha = 0 , \tag{9.4.8}$$

$$\bar{R}_{\lambda\nu} = \bar{\Gamma}_{\lambda\mu,\nu}^\mu - \bar{\Gamma}_{\lambda\nu,\mu}^\mu , \tag{9.4.9}$$

and,

$$\bar{R} = \bar{g}^{\lambda\mu}\bar{R}_{\lambda\mu} . \tag{9.4.10}$$

We remember the reader, that a geodesic system can only be defined in a given point. Just because of that, we can not conclude that the derivatives of the Christoffel symbols are null. In fact, we write, by means of the metric tensor, the expression,

$$\sqrt{g}\bar{T}_\lambda^\mu = \frac{\partial}{\partial x^\nu}\left[U_\lambda^{\mu\nu}\right] = U_{\lambda,\nu}^{\mu\nu} = \frac{1}{2}\frac{\partial}{\partial x^\nu}\left\{\frac{1}{\sqrt{g}}g_{\lambda\alpha}\left[g\left(g^{\mu\alpha}g^{\nu\beta} - g^{\nu\alpha}g^{\mu\beta}\right)\right]_{,\beta}\right\} , \tag{9.4.11}$$

and then we return back to the general frame (non-geodesic), we will find relation (9.4.4), which we reproduce below:

$$U_{\lambda,\sigma}^{\rho\sigma} = \left[\sqrt{g}T_\lambda^\rho + t_\lambda^\rho\right]. \tag{9.4.12}$$

By comparison, it results that,

$$U_\lambda^{\mu\nu} = \frac{1}{2}\left\{\frac{1}{\sqrt{g}}g_{\lambda\alpha}\left[g\left(g^{\mu\alpha}g^{\nu\beta} - g^{\nu\alpha}g^{\mu\beta}\right)\right]_{,\beta}\right\} + K_\lambda^{\mu\nu} , \tag{9.4.13}$$

where,

$K_\lambda^{\mu\nu}$ is a constant tensor.

Now, we identify, in relation (9.4.12), that the pseudo-tensor is given by the relation:

$$t_\lambda^\rho = U_{\lambda,\sigma}^{\rho\sigma} - \sqrt{g}T_\lambda^\rho . \tag{9.4.14}$$

When we derived the vacuum field equations from a variational principle in Section 9.2, we could have written,

$$I = \int R\sqrt{-g}d^4x ,$$

or,

$$I = I_2 = \int L \sqrt{-g}d^4x ,$$

$$T^{\mu\nu}{}_{;\nu} = 0.$$

In Special Relativity, the corresponding equation is:

$$\frac{\partial}{\partial x^\nu} T^{\mu\nu} = 0.$$

We now construct the tensor $M^{\alpha\beta\gamma}$:

$$M^{\gamma\alpha\beta} \equiv x^\alpha T^{\beta\gamma} - x^\beta T^{\alpha\gamma} .$$

If $T^{\mu\nu} = T^{\nu\mu}$, $M^{\gamma\alpha\beta}$ is also conserved. We may now define a "total" angular momentum,

$$J^{\alpha\beta} = \int d^3x \, M^{0\alpha\beta} = -J^{\beta\alpha} .$$

By adequately fixing the origin of our coordinate system, we may make $J^{0i} = 0$ ($i = 1, 2, 3$). Then, J^{23} , J^{31}, and J^{12} , are the components of the angular momentum, in the usual sense. As in Newtonian gravity, we may obtain the intrinsic spin, by isolating the internal part of $J^{\alpha\beta}$; in that case the spin is a constant. In order to do that, we make a translation of coordinate system:

$$x^\alpha \to x'^\alpha = x^\alpha + a^\alpha \quad ; \quad \text{we find,}$$

$$J^{\alpha\beta} \to J'^{\alpha\beta} = J^{\alpha\beta} + a^\alpha p^\beta - a^\beta p^\alpha.$$

We recognize p^α as the linear momentum, and we define the spin-vector S_α by means of:

$$S_\alpha \equiv \tfrac{1}{2}\varepsilon_{\alpha\beta\gamma\delta}J^\beta U^\delta.$$

In the above, $U^\alpha = \frac{dx^\alpha}{ds}$ (quadrivelocity), and $\varepsilon_{\alpha\beta\gamma\delta}$ is the well-known completely anti-symmetric unitary tensor.

For a free particle, then:

$$\frac{dS_\alpha}{dt} = 0.$$

In the center-of-mass system:

$$U^i = 0 \, ,$$

$$U^0 = 1 \, ,$$

$$S_1 = J^{23} \, ,$$

$$S_2 = J^{31} \, ,$$

$$S_3 = J^{12} \, ,$$

$$S_0 = 0 \, .$$

We would have, in this coordinate system:

$$U^\alpha S_\alpha = 0 \, .$$

The same above relation translates into a general coordinate system, unchanged. In General Relativity the corresponding relation $\frac{dS_\alpha}{dt} = 0$ would translate into:

$$\frac{DS_\alpha}{Ds} = 0 \, ,$$

or, if we follow Adler and Silbergleit (2000), the parallel displacement equation for the "gyro" spin vector is:

$$\frac{dS^\alpha}{ds} + \left\{ \begin{matrix} \alpha \\ \nu \ \beta \end{matrix} \right\} S^\nu \frac{dx^\beta}{ds} = 0.$$

We shall work with the first order approximation, in the velocities $\vec{v}$ and $\vec{V}$, respectively for the Earth and the gyroscope. We suppose that S^α is orthogonal to the quadrivelocity, i.e., $S^0 = 0$, in the rest frame. In another frame, in this order of approximation,

$$S^0 = \vec{S} \cdot \vec{V}.$$

In the lowest order, for the Lense-Thirring metric, the corresponding Christoffel symbols would be:

$$\left\{ \begin{matrix} 0 \\ 0 \ i \end{matrix} \right\} = \Phi_{,i} \, ,$$

$$\left\{ \begin{matrix} j \\ 0 \ 0 \end{matrix} \right\} = \Phi_{,j} \, ,$$

$$\left\{ \begin{matrix} j \\ j \ j \end{matrix} \right\} = \Phi_{,j} \, ,$$

$$\left\{ \begin{matrix} j \\ j \ i \end{matrix} \right\} = -\Phi_{,i} ,$$

$$\left\{ \begin{matrix} i \\ j \ j \end{matrix} \right\} = \Phi_{,i} \, ,$$

$$\left\{ \begin{matrix} i \\ 0 \ j \end{matrix} \right\} = \tfrac{1}{2}(h_{j,i} - h_{i,j}) \, .$$

In the above, i , $j = 1, 2, 3$, and $i \neq j$.

$$U_i^{kl} = -U_i^{lk} = \frac{g_{in}}{\sqrt{-g}} \left[-g(g^{kn}g^{lm} - g^{ln}g^{km}) \right]_{,\,m}. \tag{10.3.10}$$

When Cartesian coordinates are used, and the usual boundary conditions on the metric is found ($\lim_{r \to \infty} g_{ij} = 0$) we can define the pseudo-quadrimomentum given by:

$$P_i = \frac{1}{8\pi} \int \Theta_i^0 d^3 x. \tag{10.3.11}$$

Now we impose the slow rotating case, so that third or larger powers of $\frac{a}{r}$ can be neglected, and we find the metric tensor approximations:

$$g = -1 \, ,$$

$$g_{00} = r^{-12} \left[a^2 Q^2 r^6 (r^2 - 2z^2) + r^{10} \left(Q^2 + r^2 \right) \right] \, ,$$

$$g_{10} = \tfrac{1}{2} r^{-12} \left[2a^3 y Q^2 r^4 (3z^2 - r^2) + a^2 x Q^2 r^5 (r^2 - 5z^2) - 2ay Q^2 r^8 + 2x Q^2 r^9 \right] \, ,$$

$$g_{20} = \tfrac{1}{2} r^{-12} \left[2a^3 x Q^2 r^4 (r^2 - 3z^2) + a^2 y Q^2 r^5 (r^2 - 5z^2) + 2ax Q^2 r^8 + 2y Q^2 r^9 \right] \, ,$$

$$g_{11} = r^{-9}[a^3 xy Q^2 \left(7z^2 - r^2 \right) + a^2 Q^2 r (3y^2 z^2 + y^2 r^2 + 3z^4 - 3z^2 r^2) - 2axy Q^2 r^4 + \\ + r^5 (x^2 Q^2 - r^4)],$$

$$g_{21} = \tfrac{1}{2} r^{-9}[a^3 Q^2 (14y^2 z^2 - 2y^2 r^4 + 7z^4 - 8z^2 r^2 + r^4) - 2a^2 xy Q^2 r (r^2 - 3z^2) +$$

$$+ 2aQ^2 r^4 (x^2 - y^2) + 2xy Q^2 r^5 \right] \, , \tag{10.3.12}$$

$$g_{22} = r^{-9}[a^3 xy Q^2 (r^2 - 7z^2) + a^2 Q^2 r (r^4 - 3y^2 z^2 - y^2 r^2 - z^2 r^2) + \\ + 2axy Q^2 r^4 + r^5 (y^2 Q^2 - r^4)] \, ,$$

$$g_{30} = \tfrac{1}{2} r^{-12}[a^2 z Q^2 r^5 (3r^2 - 5z^2) + 2z Q^2 r^9] \, ,$$

$$g_{31} = \tfrac{1}{4} r^{-11}[2a^3 yz Q^3 r^3 (7z^2 - 3r^2) + 4a^2 xz Q^2 r^3 (r^2 - 3z^2) - 4ayz Q^2 r^6 + 4xz Q^2 r^7] \, ,$$

$$g_{32} = \tfrac{1}{4} r^{-11}[2a^3 xz Q^2 r^2 (3r^2 - 7z^2) + 4a^2 yz Q^2 r^3 (r^2 - 3z^2) + 4axz Q^2 r^6 + 4yz Q^2 r^7] \, ,$$

$$g_{33} = \tfrac{1}{4} r^{-12}[4a^2 z^2 Q^2 r^4 (2r^2 - 3z^2) + 4r^8 (z^2 Q^2 - r^4)] \, ,$$

$$g^{00} = r^{-6}[a^2 Q^2 (2z^2 - r^2) + r^4 (r^2 - Q^2)] \, ,$$

$$g^{10} = \tfrac{1}{2} r^{-8}[a^2 x Q^2 r (r^2 - 5z^2) + 2Q^2 r (x - ay) \, ,$$

$$g^{11} = r^{-9}[a^3 xy Q^2 (r^2 - 7z^2) + a^2 Q^2 r (3z^2 r^2 - 3y^2 z^2 - y^2 r^2 - 3z^4) + \\ + 2axy Q^2 r^4 - r^5 (r^4 - Q^2 x^2)] \, ,$$

$$g^{20} = \tfrac{1}{2}r^{-8}[2a^3xQ^2(r^2-3z^2)+a^2yQ^2r(r^2-5z^2)+2axQ^2r^4+2yQ^2r^5],$$

$$g^{21} = \tfrac{1}{2}r^{-9}[a^3Q^2(2y^2r^2-14y^2z^2-7z^2-r^4)+$$
$$+2a^2xyQ^2r(r^2+3z^2)+2aQ^2r^4(y^2-x^2-2xyQ^2r^5)],$$

$$g^{22} = \tfrac{1}{2}r^{-7}[a^3xyQ^2(7z^2-r^2)+a^2Q^2r(3y^2z^2+y^2r^2+z^2r^2-r^4)-$$
$$-2axyQ^2r^4-r^5(r^4+y^2Q^2)],$$

$$g^{30} = \tfrac{1}{2}r^{-7}[a^2zQ^2(3r^2-5z^2)+2zQ^2r^4],$$

$$g^{31} = \tfrac{1}{2}r^{-9}[a^3yzQ^2(3r^2-7z^2)+2a^2xzQ^2r(3z^2-r^2)+2zQ^2r^4(ay-xr)],$$

$$g^{32} = \tfrac{1}{2}r^{-9}[a^3xzQ^2(7z^2-3r^2)+2a^2yzQ^2r(3z^2-r^2)-2Q^2r^4z(ax+yr)],$$

$$g^{33} = r^{-8}[a^2z^2Q^2(3z^2-2r^2)-r^4(z^2Q^2+r^4)].$$

Upon obtaining the Christoffel symbols, we find the superpotential components:

$$U_0^{01} = 2r^{-8}Q^2[2a^2x(3z^2-r^2)-xr^4],$$

$$U_0^{02} = 2r^{-8}Q^2[2a^2y(3z^2-r^2)-yr^4],$$

$$U_0^{03} = 2r^{-8}Q^2[2a^2z(3z^2-2r^2)-zr^4].$$

Then, we obtain,

$$\Theta_0^0 = \tfrac{Q^2}{8\pi r^8}[r^4+2a^2(2r^2-3z^2). \tag{10.3.13}$$

Furthermore, we find:

$$P_0 = -\tfrac{Q^2}{R}[\tfrac{1}{2}+\tfrac{a^2}{3R^2}], \tag{10.3.14}$$

and, analogously,

$$P_1 = P_2 = P_3 = 0. \tag{7.3.6}$$

From the analogy with what we have said on the derivation of (10.2.10), we have to set, in place of Q^2, the expression (Q^2+M^2), and we must add to the "potential energy" terms, the inertial energy Mc^2, which we take in relativistic units with $c=1$, as:

$$P_0 = M - \left[\tfrac{Q^2+M^2}{R}\right]\left[\tfrac{a^2}{3R^2}+\tfrac{1}{2}\right]. \tag{10.3.15}$$

The last result "validates" the coordinate system chosen for the present calculation: it is tantamount to the choice of a center-of-mass coordinate system in Newtonian Physics, or the use of comoving observers in Cosmology.

repulsive gravity). We must, indeed, not confuse the "total" energy (over all space), with the energy distribution contents at radial distance from the source of the field. The "total" energy is, of course, $\lim_{R \to \infty} E = Mc^2 > 0$. We conclude that antigravity can be obtained in practice, but the total energy of a black hole is the product of the "mass parameter" M with the square of the speed of light c^2.

The most general black hole, is in fact identified by four parameters: M, Q, P, and a, which are respectively the total mass, electric and magnetic charges, and rotational parameter. The introduction of the magnetic charge has been hinted in previous Sections.

10.5.   Angular Momenta of Kerr-Newman Black Holes

[The contents of this Section is being simultaneously published by Revista Mexicana de Astronomía y Astrofísica. (Berman, 2006j)].

The calculation of energy and angular momentum of black-holes, has, among others, an important astrophysical rôle, because such objects remain the ultimate source of energy in the Universe, and the amount of angular momentum is related to the possible amount of extraction of energy from the b.h.(Levinson, 2006).

In a series of excellent papers, Virbhadra(1990; 1990a; 1990b) and Aguirregabiria et al.(1996) calculated the energy contents, as well as the angular momenta, for Kerr-Newman black-holes. Notwithstanding the high quality of those papers, Berman(2004; 2006; 2006a) has pointed out that their results for the energy do not reduce to the correct well known result by Adler et al.(1975), when the electric charge and rotation parameters go to zero. Furthermore, Berman objected the energy formula obtained by Virbhadra, and Aguirregabiria et al., because the gravitomagnetic effect on the energy contents of the Kerr-Newman black-hole does not appear in their results. Soon afterwards, Ciufolini and Pavlis(2004) and Ciufolini(2005) reported the experimental verification of the Lense-Thirring effect. This effect is a consequence of the concept of gravitomagnetism.

Therefore, it is now interesting to check whether the calculation of angular momenta contents for a K.N. black hole given by Virbhadra, and Aguirregabiria et al., includes the gravitomagnetic contribution. It will be seen that this does not occur. We recalculate here the angular momenta formulae, in order that gravitomagnetism enters into the scenario. We cite in our favor, the papers by Lynden-Bell and Katz(1985) and Katz and Ori(1990).

The metric for a K.N. black hole may be given in Cartesian coordinates by:

$$ds^2 = dt^2 - dx^2 - dy^2 - dz^2 - \frac{2\left[M - \frac{Q^2}{2r_0}\right]r_0^3}{r_0^4 + a^2 z^2} \cdot F^2 , \qquad (10.5.1)$$

while,

$$F = dt + \frac{z}{r_0}dz + \frac{r_0}{\left(r_0^2 + a^2\right)}\left(xdx + ydy\right) + \frac{a(xdy - ydx)}{a^2 + r_0^2}, \qquad (10.5.2)$$

$$r_0^4 - \left(r^2 - a^2\right)r_0^2 - a^2 z^2 = 0, \qquad (10.5.3)$$

and,

$$r^2 \equiv x^2 + y^2 + z^2 . \tag{10.5.4}$$

In the above, M, Q and "a" stand respectively for the mass, electric charge, and the rotational parameter, which has been shown to be given by:

$$a = \frac{J_{TOT}}{M}, \tag{10.5.5}$$

where J_{TOT} stands for the total angular momentum of the system, in the limit $R \to \infty$.

The cited authors obtained, for angular momentum, defined by (9.3.30):

$$J^{(3)} = \int \left[x^1 p_2 - x^2 p_1 \right] d^3 x , \tag{10.5.10}$$

and for the above metric,

$$J^{(1)} = J^{(2)} = 0 , \tag{10.5.11}$$

where p_i stand for the linear momentum densities $(i = 1, 2, 3)$.

The cited authors also found:

$$\bar{J}^{(3)} = aM - \left[\frac{Q^2}{4\rho} \right] a \left[1 - \frac{\rho^2}{a^2} + \frac{(a^2+\rho^2)^2}{a^3\rho} arctgh \left(\frac{a}{\rho} \right) \right], \tag{10.5.12}$$

and when we go to the slow rotation case, Virbhadra found:

$$\bar{J}^{(3)} \cong aM - 2Q^2 a \left[\frac{a^2}{5R^3} + \frac{1}{3R} \right] . \tag{10.5.13}$$

Unfortunately, when $Q = 0$ in the above equations, we are left without gravitomagnetic effects. The corrections made by Berman, in the above cited papers, reside on the acknowledgment that due to the same R^{-2} dependence of the gravitation and electric interactions, as characterized by Newton's law of gravitation, and Coulomb's law for electric charges, we would have on a par, the equal contributions of charge and mass in the above formulae, so that, except for the inclusion of the inertial term, we should make the correction:

$$Q^2 \to Q^2 + M^2 + P^2 . \tag{10.5.14}$$

In corroboration of correction (10.5.14), we cite that, for the Reissner-Nordström metric, the energy formula is given by:

$$E_{RN} = M - \left[\frac{Q^2 + M^2 + P^2}{2R} \right] . \tag{10.5.15}$$

Relation(10.5.15) reduces correctly to the energy formula published by Adler et al.(1975) for the spherical mass distribution, when we make $Q = P = 0$ in (10.5.15). To the contrary, relations (10.5.6) and (10.5.8) do not reduce to Adler et al.'s formula when

$$S^{1201} = \frac{Q^2}{2} r^{-8} \left[2a^3 x (r^2 - 3z^2) + a^2 yr(r^2 - 5z^2) + 2axr^4 + 2yr^5 \right].$$

$$S^{1202} = \frac{Q^2}{2} r^{-8} \left[2a^3 y(r^2 - 3z^2) + a^2 xr(5z^2 - r^2) + 2ayr^4 - 2xr^5 \right].$$

$$S^{1301} = \frac{Q^2}{2} r^{-7} \left[a^2 z(3r^2 - 5z^2) + 2zr^4 \right]. \tag{10.5.28}$$

$$S^{1303} = \frac{Q^2}{2} r^{-8} \left[2a^3 y(r^2 - 3z^2) + a^2 xr(5z^2 - r^2) + 2ayr^4 - 2xr^5 \right].$$

$$S^{3202} = \frac{Q^2}{2} r^{-7} \left[a^2 z(5z^2 - 3r^2) - 2zr^4 \right]$$

$$S^{3203} = \frac{Q^2}{2} r^{-8} \left[2a^3 x(r^2 - 3z^2) + a^2 yr(r^2 - 5z^2) + 2axr^4 + 2yr^5 \right].$$

$$S^{1203} = S^{1302} = S^{2301} = 0$$

We now obtain the momentum densities,

$$P^x = \frac{2}{\kappa} r^{-10} Q^2 \left[3a^3 y(r^2 - 2z^2) + ayr^4 \right]. \tag{10.5.29a}$$

$$P^y = \frac{2}{\kappa} r^{-10} Q^2 \left[3a^3 x(2z^2 - r^2) - axr^4 \right]. \tag{10.5.29b}$$

$$P^z = 0. \tag{10.5.29c}$$

Following the treatment in last Chapter, we find now, from the general formula:

$$J^\alpha = \int \left(x^\beta P^\gamma - x^\gamma P^\beta \right) dx dy dz, \tag{10.5.30}$$

where, α, β and γ take successive cyclic values 1, 2 and 3.

OBTAINING THE GENERAL FORMULA

We find then, by making right now $Q^2 \rightarrow \left[Q^2 + M^2 + P^2 \right]$,

$$J^z = -2a \left[Q^2 + M^2 + P^2 \right] \left[\frac{1}{3R} + \frac{a^2}{5R^3} \right]. \tag{10.5.31}$$

$$J^x = J^y = 0. \tag{10.5.32}$$

We must remember, that, due to the inertial part, which is in fact the limiting result, when $R \rightarrow \infty$, we must add the term Ma in the angular momentum formula for J^z, which now becomes :

$$J^z = Ma - 2a \left[Q^2 + M^2 + P^2 \right] \left[\frac{1}{3R} + \frac{a^2}{5R^3} \right]. \tag{10.5.33}$$

We now could study the appearance of gravitomagnetic contributions to angular momenta, and we would also correct the results by Virbhadra (1990 , 1990 a, 1990 b) and Aguirregabiria et al. (1996). This was done by Berman (2006 j), and, in the slow rotation case, it was found a gravitomagnetic contribution to the angular momentum of:

$$\Delta J \cong -2M^2 \left[\frac{a^3}{5R^3} + \frac{a}{3R} \right]. \tag{10.5.34}$$

The general formula, valid for any rotational parameter, should likewise become (10.5.20) above.

10.6.   On the Energy of the Universe

The zero-total-energy of the Roberston-Walker's Universe, was demonstrated by many authors (Berman 2006, 2006a, 2006b, 2006c).

It may be that the Universe might have originated from a vacuum quantum fluctuation. In support of this view, we shall show that the pseudotensor theory (Adler et al, 1975) points out to a null-energy for a Robertson-Walker-flat Universe, in a Cartesian-coordinates calculation. (Berman, 2006, 2006 a; Rosen, 1995; York Jr, 1980; Cooperstock, 1994; Cooperstock and Israelit, 1995). Next, we shall show that in spherical coordinates, we would obtain a wrong result, but see also references (Katz, 2006; 1985; and Ori, 1990; et al, 1997). Near 2004, Frank Columbus invited me to contribute for two Nova Science edited books, where I have shown that Robertson-Walker's metric must refer to a zero-total energy Universe. (Berman, 2006; 2006a).

Flat Robertson-Walker's Energy:

It has been generally accepted that the Universe has zero-total energy. The first such claim, as far as the present author recollects, was due to Feynman(1962-3). Lately, Berman(2006, 2006 a) has proved this result by means of simple arguments involving Robertson-Walker's metric for any value of the tri-curvature ($0, -1, 1$).

The pseudotensor t_v^μ, also called Einstein's pseudotensor, is such that, when summed with the energy-tensor of matter T_v^μ, gives the following conservation law:

$$\left[\sqrt{-g}\left(T_v^\mu + t_v^\mu\right)\right]_{,\mu} = 0 .$$ (10.6.1)

In such case, the quantity

$$P_\mu = \left\{\sqrt{-g}\left[T_\mu^0 + t_\mu^0\right]\right\} d^3x ,$$ (10.6.2)

is called the general-relativistic generalization of the energy-momentum four-vector of special relativity (Adler et al, 1975).

It can be proved that P_μ is conserved when:

a) $T_v^\mu \neq 0$ only in a finite part of space; and,
b) $g_{\mu\nu} \to \eta_{\mu\nu}$ when we approach infinity, where $\eta_{\mu\nu}$ is the Minkowski metric tensor.

However, there is no reason to doubt that, even if the above conditions were not fulfilled, we might eventually get a constant P_μ, because the above conditions are sufficient, but not strictly necessary. In Part Three, we hint on the plausibility of other conditions, instead of a) and b) above.

Such a case will occur, for instance, when we have the integral in (10.6.2) is equal to zero.

For R.W.'s flat metric, we get exactly this result, because, from Freud's (1939) formulae, we have

$$P_v = \frac{1}{2\kappa} \int \sqrt{-g} \{ \, [\, \delta_v^0 \left(g^{\beta\alpha}\Gamma_{\beta\rho}^\rho - g^{\beta\rho}\Gamma_{\beta\rho}^\alpha \right) + \delta_v^\alpha \left(g^{\beta\rho}\Gamma_{\rho\beta}^0 - g^{0\rho}\Gamma_{\rho\beta}^\beta \right) -$$

$$- \left(g^{\beta\alpha}\Gamma_{\beta v}^0 - g^{\beta 0}\Gamma_{\beta v}^\alpha \right)] \} \,_{,\alpha} d^3x \tag{10.6.3}$$

From R.W.'s flat metric,

$$ds^2 = dt^2 - R^2(t)d\sigma^2 \,, \tag{10.6.4}$$

we find that

$$g^{ii}\Gamma_{ii}^0 \equiv g^{00}\Gamma_{0i}^i, \tag{10.6.5}$$

and, then,

$$P_i = 0 \qquad\qquad (\, i = 1,2,3 \,)\,. \tag{10.6.6}$$

On the other hand, considering only the non-vanishing Christoffel symbols, we would find:

$$P_0 = \frac{1}{2\kappa} \int \sqrt{-g} \left[g^{jj}\Gamma_{ji}^i - g^{ii}\Gamma_{ii}^j \right]_{,j} d^3x. \tag{10.6.7}$$

And from the last relation, and (10.6.4), we obtain,

$$P_0 = 0 \,. \tag{10.6.8}$$

Because we found a constant result, we may say that the total energy of a flat R.W.'s Universe is null.

A different calculation, as follows, leads to the same result. Weinberg(1972) defines:

$$h_{\mu\nu} \equiv g_{\mu\nu} - \eta_{\mu\nu} \,, \tag{10.6.9}$$

and then solves for the 4-pseudo-momentum, obtaining:

$$P^j = -\frac{1}{16\pi G} \int \left\{ -\frac{\partial h_{kk}}{\partial t}\delta^{ij} + \frac{\partial h_{k0}}{\partial x^k}\delta_{ij} - \frac{\partial h_{j0}}{\partial x^i} + \frac{\partial h_{ij}}{\partial t} \right\} \left\{ n_i r^2 d\Omega \right\} \,, \tag{10.6.10}$$

and,

$$P^0 = -\frac{1}{16\pi G} \int \left\{ \frac{\partial h_{jj}}{\partial x^i} - \frac{\partial h_{ij}}{\partial x^j} \right\} \left\{ n_i r^2 d\Omega \right\} \,, \tag{10.6.11}$$

with

$$d\Omega = \sin\theta d\theta d\phi, \tag{10.6.12a}$$

and,

$$n_i \equiv \tfrac{x_i}{r}. \tag{10.6.12b}$$

Though (10.6.10) and (10.6.11) can be constants in the case considered in Weinberg's book, it is evident that if the integrals in both (10.6.10) and (10.6.11) are null, we still can call the null result of (10.6.11) as a proof of the null energy of the R.W. flat Universe. And, in this case,

$$P^i = P^0 = 0 \qquad (\; i = 1,2,3 \;). \tag{10.6.13}$$

A similar result would be obtained from Landau-Lifshitz pseudotensor (1975), where we have:

$$P_{LL}^v = \int (-g) \left[T^{v0} + t_L^{v0} \right] \, d^3x, \tag{10.6.14}$$

where,

$$(-g)t_L^{ik} = \tfrac{1}{2\kappa} \{ \; g_{,l}^{ik} \, g_{,m}^{lm} - g_{,l}^{il} \, g_{,m}^{km} + \tfrac{1}{2} g^{ik} g_{lm} g^{ln}_{,\rho} g^{\rho m}_{,n} - (g^{il} g_{mn} g^{kn}_{,\rho} g^{m\rho}_{,l} + g^{kl} g_{mn} g^{in}_{,\rho} g^{m\rho}_{,l}) +$$

$$+ \; g_{lm} g^{n\rho} g^{il}_{,n} g^{km}_{,p} + \tfrac{1}{8} (2 g^{il} g^{km} - g^{ik} g^{lm})(2 g_{n\rho} g_{qr} - g_{\rho q} g_{nr}) g^{nr}_{,l} g^{pq}_{,m} \; \},$$

(in this last expression all indices run from 0 to 3). (10.6.17)

A short calculation shows that:

$$P_{LL}^v = 0 \qquad (\, v = 0,1,2,3 \;). \tag{10.6.16}$$

The above results could also follow from superpotential formulae (Freud, 1939). For instance, from the Einstein's superpotential:

$$P_v = \int \left[U_v^{[0\sigma]} \right]_{,\sigma} d^3x \; ,$$

where,

$$2\kappa \sqrt{-g} U_v^{[\mu\rho]}_{(E)} = g_{v\sigma} \left\{ g \left[g^{\mu\sigma} g^{\rho\lambda} - g^{\mu\lambda} g^{\rho\sigma} \right] \right\}_{,\lambda} \; .$$

Then, we find, for the Robertson-Walker's metric,

$$U_v^{[0\sigma]}_{(E)} = 0 \qquad (\; v = 0,1,2,3 \;).$$

Then, $P_0 = 0$. Analogously, we would find $P_i = 0$.

Closed Robertson-Walker's Counter-Example:

We can give a counter-example, showing that if we do not use Cartesian coordinates, but other system, say, spherical coordinates, the energy calculation becomes flawed (Berman,

1981), as it has been warned by Weinberg(1972) and Adler, Bazin and Schiffer(1975), among others.

Consider a closed Robertson-Walker's metric:

$$ds^2 = -\frac{R^2(t)}{\left(1+\frac{r^2}{4}\right)^2}\left[dr^2 + r^2 d\theta^2 + r^2 \sin^2\theta d\phi^2\right] + dt^2 . \tag{10.6.17}$$

With the energy momentum tensor for a perfect fluid, whose comoving components are:

$$T_0^0 = \rho,$$

$$T_1^1 = T_2^2 = T_3^3 = -p ,$$

$$T_\nu^\mu = 0 \quad \text{if} \quad \mu \neq \nu ,$$

where ρ and p stand for energy density and cosmic pressure, respectively, and with a pseudo-tensor given by:

$$\sqrt{-g}t_\beta^\alpha = \frac{1}{2\kappa}\left[\delta_\beta^\alpha U - g_{,\beta}^{\mu\nu}\frac{\partial U}{\partial g_{,\alpha}^{\mu\nu}}\right] , \tag{10.6.18}$$

where,

$$U = \sqrt{-g}g^{\mu\nu}\left[\Gamma_{\mu\alpha}^\beta\Gamma_{\nu\beta}^\alpha - \Gamma_{\mu\nu}^\alpha\Gamma_{\alpha\beta}^\beta\right] , \tag{10.6.19}$$

we shall find a time-varying result for the energy.

If we consider Einstein's field equations, with $k = +1$, where k is the tricurvature, in particular we have:

$$3H^2 = \kappa\rho - 3R^{-2}, \tag{10.6.20}$$

with,

$$H = \frac{\dot{R}}{R} \quad \text{(Hubble's parameter)} .$$

Then we find after a short calculation:

$$U = \sqrt{-g}\left[6H^2 - \frac{2}{r^2R^2}\left(1 - \frac{r^2}{R^2}\right)^2\right] ,$$

and, then we find:

$$P_0 = \frac{4\pi^2}{\kappa}R(t) .$$

$$P_1 = P_2 = P_3 = 0 .$$

The time-varying result for P_0 shows that only Cartesian coordinates must be employed when applying pseudotensors in General Relativity. In reference (York Jr, 1980) it is stated that, for closed Universes, the only acceptable result is $P_0 = 0$. See also Part Four below.

Flat Robertson-Walker's Counter-Example:

We now repeat succinctly the $k = 0$ calculation, employing polar spherical coordinates, finding the wrong result $P_0 = \infty$.

Consider Einstein's pseudotensor, as in Part One above. We shall find:

$$U = 6\sqrt{-g}H^2 - \frac{2}{r^2 R^2};$$

and,

$$P_0 = \int \sqrt{-g}\left[\frac{3}{\kappa R^2} - \frac{1}{\kappa r^2 R^2}\right] d^3x,$$

where,

$$\sqrt{-g} = R^3 r^2 \sin\theta.$$

We find then,

$$P_0 = \lim_{r \to \infty} \int \frac{3Rr^2\sin\theta}{\kappa}\left[1 - \frac{1}{3r^2}\right]d^3x = \lim_{r \to \infty}\int \frac{3Rr^2\sin\theta}{\kappa}\left[1 - \frac{1}{3r^2}\right]r^2\sin\theta \, d\theta \, d\phi \, dr.$$

In the process of integration we will find:

$$\int_0^\infty \left(r^4 - \tfrac{1}{3}r^2\right) dr = \infty.$$

This shows again, that Cartesian coordinates should be employed.

A Counter-counter example:

While we have shown that Cartesian coordinates yield acceptable results, and spherical coordinates may lead to inconsistencies, we shall now show that LL pseudotensor yields a correct zero result for the energy of a closed Robertson-Walker's Universe, even if spherical coordinates are used (Berman, 1981).

According to Landau-Lifshitz pseudotensor, we would have:

$$P^\mu = \int (-g)\left[T^{\mu 0} + t_{LL}^{\mu 0}\right] d^3x.$$

We apply now the superpotential:

$$(-g)\left[T^{\mu 0} + t_{LL}^{\mu 0}\right] = U_{LL}^{\mu[\nu\sigma]}{}_{,\sigma},$$

where,

$$U^{\mu[\nu\sigma]}_{LL} = \tfrac{1}{2\kappa}\tfrac{\partial}{\partial x^{\lambda}}\left[(-g)\left(g^{\mu\nu}g^{\sigma\lambda} - g^{\mu\sigma}g^{\nu\sigma}\right)\right].$$

We then find successively,

$$P^{0} = \tfrac{1}{2\kappa}\int \tfrac{\partial^{2}}{\partial x^{\sigma}\partial x^{\lambda}}\left[(-g)\left(g^{00}g^{\sigma\lambda} - g^{0\sigma}g^{0\lambda}\right)\right]d^{3}x \qquad =$$

$$= \tfrac{1}{2\kappa}\int \tfrac{\partial^{2}}{\partial r^{2}}\left[-g_{22}g_{33}\right]d^{3}x + \tfrac{1}{2\kappa}\int \tfrac{\partial^{2}}{\partial \theta^{2}}\left[-g_{11}g_{33}\right]d^{3}x \qquad = 0,$$

where we have made use of the following results:

$$\int_{0}^{\pi} \tfrac{\partial}{\partial\theta^{2}}\left(\sin^{2}\theta\right)d\theta = 2\int_{0}^{\pi}\cos 2\theta d\theta = \tfrac{1}{2}\left[\sin 2\theta\right]_{0}^{\pi} = 0.$$

and,

$$\left\{\tfrac{d}{dr}\tfrac{r^{4}}{\left[\left(1+\tfrac{r^{2}}{4}\right)^{4}\right]}\right\}_{0}^{\infty} = \left\{\tfrac{4r^{3}}{\left(1+\tfrac{r^{2}}{4}\right)^{4}} - \tfrac{2r^{5}}{\left(1+\tfrac{r^{2}}{4}\right)^{5}}\right\}_{0}^{\infty} = 0.$$

Analogously we would find that the space components of the pseudomomentum are null.

Conclusions :

The importance of our results, lie in the fact that flat Universes enjoy a preferred status for the inflationary scenario (Guth, 1981). The zero result for the spatial components of the energy-momentum-pseudotensor calculation, are equivalent to the choice of a center of Mass reference system in Newtonian theory, likewise the use of comoving observers in Cosmology. It is with this idea in mind, that we are led to the energy calculation, yielding zero total energy, for the Universe, as an acceptable result: we are assured that we chose the correct reference system; this is a response to the criticism made by some scientists which argue that pseudotensor calculations depend on the reference system, and thus, those calculations are devoid of physical meaning.

The counter-example ($k = +1$) shows, nevertheless, that Cartesian coordinates need to be used. Next, a new counter-example ($k = 0$) shows the same problem. In the following calculation, we found a counter-counter-example, where the use of spherical coordinates, although tragic earlier, does no harm in the Landau-Lifshitz calculation. We thank J.Katz, for several advises, in order to allow any kind of coordinates in energy calculations, and that superpotentials should be preferred, because our calculations would be simplified (Katz, 2006, 1985; and Ori, 1990; et al, 1997).

10.7.   Energy and Angular Momentum of Dilaton Black Holes

Scalar fields may alter our view of the Universe. Kaluza-Klein theory, contains a scalar field arising from the pentadimensional 5-5 component of the metric tensor (Wesson, 1999; 2006). Such scalar field, generally named as *dilatons,* were also identified with inflationary model's *inflaton* (Collins, Martin and Squires, 1989). String and brane theories, deal with *dilatons* which play rôles similar to the gravitons. String theories have compactified internal space, whose size arises a *dilaton,* or scalar field. Altogether, it has been claimed that gravitons interact among themselves and may have also scalar field companions. Etc...

The calculation of energy and angular momentum of black-holes, has, among others, an important astrophysical rôle, because such objects remain the ultimate source of energy in the Universe, and the amount of angular momentum is related to the possible amount of extraction of energy from the b.h.(Levinson, 2006).

Therefore, Berman(2006j), checked whether the calculation of energy and angular momenta contents for a K.N. black hole given by Virbhadra, and Aguirregabiria et al., included the gravitomagnetic contribution. It was seen that this did not occur. Berman recalculated the energy and angular momenta formulae, in order that gravitomagnetism enters into the scenario. In the present text, we advance the theoretical framework, by studying the effect of a *dilaton* or scalar field, within Black holes.

Chamorro and Virbhadra (1996) have calculated the energy of a spherically symmetric charged non-rotating *dilaton* black hole, which obeys the metric,

$$ds^2 = A\ ^1 dt^2 - A dr^2 - Dr^2 (d\Omega^2) .$$ (10.7.1)

Garfinkle, Horowitz, and Strominger (1991; 1992) departed from a variational principle which included a scalar field Φ , and the electromagnetic tensor $F_{\alpha\beta}$, in addition to the Ricci scalar R , to wit,

$$\delta \int \left[-R + 2(\nabla\Phi)^2 + e^{-2\beta\Phi} F^2 \right] \sqrt{-g} d^4 x = 0 .$$ (10.7.2)

The resultant field equations are:

$$\nabla_j \left(e^{-2\beta\Phi} F^{jk} \right) = 0,$$

$$\nabla^2 \Phi + \tfrac{\beta}{2} e^{-2\beta\Phi} F^2 = 0,$$
$$R_{ij} = 2\nabla_i \Phi \nabla_j \Phi + 2 e^{-2\beta\Phi} F_{ia} F_j^a - \tfrac{1}{2} g_{ij} e^{-2\beta\Phi} F^2,$$

and, the *dilaton* was described by the following solution:

$$e^{-2\Phi} = \left[1 - \tfrac{r_-}{r} \right]^{\frac{1-\sigma}{\beta}} .$$ (10.7.3)

The sign of β only influences the sign of Φ ; we are going therefore to take $\beta > 0$.

The usual Coulomb interaction is given by,

$$F_{0r} = \tfrac{Q}{r^2} .$$ (10.7.4)

The metric coefficients are,

$$A^{-1} = \left(1 - \frac{r_+}{r}\right)\left(1 - \frac{r_-}{r}\right)^{\sigma}, \quad (10.7.5)$$

and,

$$D = \left(1 - \frac{r_-}{r}\right)^{1-\sigma}. \tag{10.7.6}$$

In the above, we have made use of the following constraints and/or definitions,

$$\sigma = \frac{1-\beta^2}{1+\beta^2}. \tag{10.7.7}$$

$$r_+ + \sigma r_- \equiv 2M. \tag{10.7.8}$$

$$r_+ r_- \equiv Q^2\left(1 + \beta^2\right). \tag{10.7.9}$$

It can be seen that β rules the coupling intensity among the three fields, gravitational, electromagnetic and scalar.

The lesson given by Berman(2006j), was that when energy or momentum were calculated, it sufficed to take the charge contribution, leaving $M = 0$, and, at the end of pseudotensorial calculation, make the following transformation:

$$Q^2 \rightarrow \left[Q^2 + M^2 + P^2\right]. \tag{10.7.10}$$

Of course, there should be made room for the inertial content, Mc^2 in the case of the energy, and aM, in the case of rotating black hole's angular momentum: these two terms were the total energy or momentum, when $r \rightarrow \infty$.

For instance, if the electric energy of Reissner-Nordström's black hole was given by $-\frac{Q^2}{2r}$, the total contributions for the energy content would be written as,

$$E_{RN} = Mc^2 - \frac{\left[Q^2 + M^2 + P^2\right]}{2r}. \tag{10.7.11}$$

When a scalar field of the above form enters into the scene, Chamorro and Virbhadra (1996) found, by pseudo-tensor calculations, for the electric contribution, the term, $-\frac{Q^2}{2r}\left(1 - \beta^2\right)$. Therefore, by means of our rule, we have the complete formula as given by,

$$E = Mc^2 - \frac{\left[Q^2 + M^2 + P^2\right]}{2r}\left(1 - \beta^2\right). \tag{10.7.12}$$

We now turn our attention to the rotating charged situation. By analogy with the above case, consider that, for a K.N. black hole, the metric may be given in Cartesian coordinates by:

$$ds^2 = dt^2 - dx^2 - dy^2 - dz^2 - \frac{2\left[M - \frac{Q^2}{2r_0}\right]r_0^3}{r_0^4 + a^2 z^2} \cdot \overline{F}^2, \tag{10.7.13}$$

while,

$$\bar{F} = dt + \frac{Z}{r_0}dz + \frac{r_0}{(r_0^2 + a^2)}(xdx + ydy) + \frac{a(xdy - ydx)}{a^2 + r_0^2}, \tag{10.7.14}$$

$$r_0^4 - (r^2 - a^2)r_0^2 - a^2z^2 = 0, \tag{10.7.15}$$

and,

$$r^2 \equiv x^2 + y^2 + z^2. \tag{10.7.16}$$

In the above, M, Q and "a" stand respectively for the mass, electric charge, and the rotational parameter, which has been shown to be given by:

$$a = \frac{J_{TOT}}{M}, \tag{10.7.17}$$

where J_{TOT} stands for the total angular momentum of the system, in the limit $R \to \infty$. As Berman (2006j) described in his recent paper, we may take the electric energy calculations by Virbhadra (1990; 1990a; 1990b) and Aguirregabiria et al. (1996), and, by applying the transformation (10.7.10), obtaining, for the energy and angular momenta, the formulae of Sections 10.3 and 10.5 above;

$$(P_0)_{KN} = M - \left[\frac{Q^2 + M^2 + P^2}{4\rho}\right]\left[1 + \frac{(a^2 + \rho^2)}{a\rho}arctgh\left(\frac{a}{\rho}\right)\right], \tag{10.7.18}$$

$$P_1 = P_2 = P_3 = 0. \tag{10.7.19}$$

Likewise, if we apply:
$$J^{(3)} = \int \left[x^1 p_2 - x^2 p_1\right]d^3x,$$

we find,

$$\left(J^{(3)}\right)_{KN} = aM - \left[\frac{Q^2 + M^2 + P^2}{4\rho}\right]a\left[1 - \frac{\rho^2}{a^2} + \frac{(a^2 + \rho^2)^2}{a^3\rho}arctgh\left(\frac{a}{\rho}\right)\right]. \tag{10.7.20}$$

$$J^{(1)} = J^{(2)} = 0. \tag{10.7.21}$$

We now are able to write the corresponding result, for a *dilaton* Kerr-Newman black hole's energy and momenta, where, the linear momentum densities are given by:

$$p_1 = -2\left(1 - \beta^2\right)\left[\frac{(Q^2 + M^2 + P^2)\rho^4}{8\pi(\rho^4 + a^2z^2)^3}\right]ay\rho^2,$$

$$p_2 = -2\left(1 - \beta^2\right)\left[\frac{(Q^2 + M^2 + P^2)\rho^4}{8\pi(\rho^4 + a^2z^2)^3}\right]ax\rho^2,$$

$p_3 = 0$,

while the energy density is given by:

$$\mu = \left(1 - \beta^2\right) \left[\frac{(Q^2 + M^2 + P^2)\rho^4}{8\pi(\rho^4 + a^2 z^2)^3}\right] \left(\rho^4 + 2a^2\rho^2 - a^2 z^2\right).$$

$$(P_0)_{dilaton} = M - \left[\frac{Q^2 + M^2 + P^2}{4\rho}\right]\left[1 + \frac{(a^2 + \rho^2)}{a\rho} arctgh\left(\frac{a}{\rho}\right)\right]\left(1 - \beta^2\right),\qquad (10.7.22)$$

$$P_1 = P_2 = P_3 = 0. \qquad (10.7.23)$$

$$\left(J^{(3)}\right)_{dilaton} = aM - \left[\frac{Q^2 + M^2 + P^2}{4\rho}\right]a\left[1 - \frac{\rho^2}{a^2} + \frac{(a^2 + \rho^2)^2}{a^3\rho} arctgh\left(\frac{a}{\rho}\right)\right]\left(1 - \beta^2\right). \qquad (10.7.24)$$

$$J^{(1)} = J^{(2)} = 0. \qquad (10.7.25)$$

Relations (10.7.23) and (10.7.25), "validate" the coordinate system chosen for the present calculation: it is tantamount to the choice of a center-of-mass coordinate system in Newtonian Physics, or the use of comoving observers in Cosmology.

In (10.7.22) and (10.7.24), we have included a magnetic "charge" P, and the factor $\left(1 - \beta^2\right)$, which makes for the scalar field interaction. In fact, our "naive" trick, was to make the following transformation,

$$Q^2 \rightarrow \left[Q^2 + M^2 + P^2\right]\left(1 - \beta^2\right), \qquad (10.7.26)$$

which takes us from the black hole charge contribution, to the total scalar field – electromagnetic charges – gravitation field contributions, which constitute the *dilaton* Kerr-Newman black hole!!!

That our trick "works", is a question of applying, say, Einstein's superpotential calculations. But, again, we can be sure that our formulae keeps intact the following physical good properties:

1) gravitomagnetic effects are explicit;
2) the triple coupling, among scalar, gravitational and electromagnetic fields becomes evident; and,
3) when $\beta = 1$, the scalar field neutralizes the other interactions; if $\beta < 1$, the neutralization is only partial.

By considering an expansion of the $\text{arcth}(\frac{a}{\rho})$ function, in terms of increasing powers of the parameter "a", and by neglecting terms $\left(\frac{a}{\rho}\right)^{3+n} \simeq 0$, (with $n = 0, 1, 2, \ldots$) we find the energy of a slowly rotating *dilaton* Kerr-Newman black-hole,

$$E \simeq M - \left[\frac{Q^2 + M^2 + P^2}{R}\right]\left[\frac{a^2}{3R^2} + \frac{1}{2}\right]\left(1 - \beta^2\right), \qquad (10.7.27)$$

where $\rho \to R$; this can be seen because the defining equation for ρ is:

$$\frac{x^2+y^2}{\rho^2+a^2} + \frac{z^2}{\rho^2} = 1$$

and if $a \to 0$, $\rho \to R$.

We can interpret the terms $\frac{(Q^2+P^2)a^2(1-\beta^2)}{3R^3}$ and $\frac{M^2a^2(1-\beta^2)}{3R^3}$ as the magnetic and gravitomagnetic energies caused by rotation.

Expanding the *arctgh* function in powers of $(\frac{a}{\rho})$, and retaining up to third power, we find the slow rotation angular momentum:

$$J^{(3)} \cong aM - 2\left[Q^2+M^2+P^2\right]a\left[\frac{a^2}{5R^3} + \frac{1}{3R}\right](1-\beta^2). \tag{10.7.28}$$

In the same approximation, we would find:

$$\mu \cong \left[\frac{Q^2+M^2+P^2}{4\pi R^4}\right]\left[\frac{a^2}{R^2} + \frac{1}{2}\right](1-\beta^2). \tag{10.7.29}$$

The above formula could be also found by applying directly the definition,

$$\mu = \frac{dP_0}{dV} = \frac{1}{4\pi R^2}\frac{dP_0}{dR}. \tag{10.7.30}$$

We further conclude that we may identify the gravitomagnetic contribution to the energy and angular momentum of the *dilaton* K.N. black hole, for the slow rotating case, as:

$$\Delta E \cong -\frac{M^2a^2}{3R^3}(1-\beta^2), \tag{10.7.31}$$

and,

$$\Delta J \cong -2M^2\left[\frac{a^3}{5R^3} + \frac{a}{3R}\right](1-\beta^2) \approx -\frac{2M^2a}{3R}(1-\beta^2), \tag{10.7.32}$$

as can be easily checked by the reader.

It is important to notice that the contributed energy, due to the scalar field is given by the term $\frac{\beta^2}{2r}\left[M^2+Q^2+P^2\right] > 0$, but the corresponding energy density is negative, given by $-\left[\frac{\beta^2[M^2+Q^2+P^2]}{8\pi R^4}\right]$. This negative energy density, is the trademark of the scalar field. It must be remarked that all of our results do not match with Chamorro and Virbhadra's, except in the particular case when $M = P = 0$. Of course, those authors only examined the Reissner-Nordströns *dilaton*. The latter authors only dealt with this non-rotating case. We also found that there is no decoupling between matter, charges and the scalar field. The comment by Brans and Dicke(1961) about the decoupling between scalar fields and matter, is cast by us in doubt.

We remember that the terms Mc^2 and aM which appear respectively, in the energy and momentum formulae, refer to inertia and not to gravitation: thus, they refer to Special Relativity. We have found also, that the scalar field reduces the self-energies, of gravitation and electromagnetic origin, by a factor $(1 - \beta^2)$.

Part V

MACH'S PRINCIPLE

valid, each one of both observers could tell to the other one: "I am at rest, and you are in rotational motion". This is not verifiable in Newtonian physics because one of those observers faces acceleration, while the other one does not. Consequently, Newton, in order to save the relativity principle, postulated the existence of an absolute observer so that he could distinguish Σ from Σ'. The presence of an acceleration in Σ' and not in Σ, is due to the existence of an absolute space, relative to which a given referential can either be accelerated or not. But as Einstein (1923) observed, this does not put the principle of causality in a safe ground. We conclude that, within the Newtonian theory of absolute space, the principle of causality becomes mutilated. The reader should remember that Einstein substituted, in Special Relativity, absolute time, and absolute space, for an absolute spacetime, represented by an invariant line element (Minkowski's). In General Relativity Theory, this "absolutism", was reduced to a local concept, in a Riemannian space. But, Newton's *absolute time* is different from our *cosmic time*.

Next, we shall follow arguments against a theory made up from Newtonian gravitational theory.

Objections to Newton's Gravity

The basis for Newtonian Cosmology is Poisson's equation for the gravitational field. For readers not familiar with this equation we refer to basic university physics texts, where, in electrostatics, there is an analogous equation:

$$\nabla^2 U = 4\pi G\rho .$$ (11.1.1)

The above equation for the Universe, presupposes that matter is continuously distributed with mass density ρ, while G stands for Newton's gravitational constant and U is the gravitational potential. We justify the matter hypothesis above, because the mass distribution is extended over cosmic distances.

Einstein showed that this equation does not substitute perfectly the action-at-a-distance gravitational law because of the boundary conditions for the solution of the equation. In other words, we have to impose boundary conditions for the gravitational potential U at infinity. The solution of Poisson's equation requires that, when $r \to \infty$, we should have $\lim_{r\to\infty} U = U_\infty =$ fixed value. We conclude that $\lim_{r\to\infty} \rho = 0$.

Nevertheless, we know that $U \sim r^{-1}$ (Halliday, Resnick and Walker, 2005). So $\rho \sim r^{-3}$. This means that ρ goes to zero more rapidly than U, for large values of r. This behavior led Einstein to say that Newtonian cosmology models possesses infinite mass, but in some sense it is finite because the gravitational potential goes to zero more slowly than the density!!! Let us now examine why Poisson's equation was not acceptable to Einstein in the cosmological domain.

First: the inhomogeneity due to $\rho \sim r^{-3}$ is incompatible with astronomical observations.

Second: it includes the notion of "center of the Universe" which is meaningless.

Third: Einstein shows that $\rho \sim r^{-3}$ is against statistical physics theory. The boundary condition imposes - as we saw – to Poisson's equation, that $\lim_{r \to \infty} U = U_\infty$ = fixed value. Now, by statistical physics, each astronomical object could acquire kinetic energy enough to overcome this value and then disappear towards infinity. Thus we would not find $\rho \sim r^{-3}$. We see therefore, that the static character of this Universe which is represented by Poisson's equation, is inviable.

Fourth: We could find an alternative solution ρ = constant, but this can not be sustained by Poisson's equation because the gravitational potential U would become undetermined. This objection was presented by Seeliger in the year 1895, as cited in North (1965).

Fifth: In order to make superseded, the Seeliger's objection, it could be suggested that there is a universal constant λ , in a modified Poisson's equation, namely:

$$\nabla^2 U \quad \lambda U = 4\pi G \rho .\qquad (11.1.2)$$

A possible solution to this equation would be:

$$U = -\frac{4\pi G}{\lambda}\rho ,\qquad (11.1.3)$$

with ρ = constant.

However this modification introduces a new constant λ by means of an ad-hoc hypothesis. This runs against the theoretical framework.

Sixth: As Einstein observed, the radiating energy is originated by mass and it gets lost into infinity, which is also incompatible with the hypothesis $\rho \sim r^{-3}$.

Seventh: The functions $U \sim r^{-1}$, and $\rho \sim r^{-3}$, carry a nonsense: at infinity we would have a constant value U_∞ and the absence of mass because ρ goes to zero faster than U goes to U_∞ . Einstein interpreted this hypothesis as being a universe with infinite mass, contained in a finite volume. Obviously, the mathematics is inconsistent: a universe in which $\lim_{r \to \infty} U = U_\infty$ = constant, with $\rho_\infty = 0$, while $U \sim r^{-1}$ and $\rho \sim r^{-3}$, gives us the idea that there is an exterior space outside the universe, because in physical theory we can not speak rigorously about infinities. When we say that $\lim_{r \to \infty} \rho = 0$, we simply represent mathematically the idea that for large distances r , the density goes to zero. Therefore such infinite limit brings about the concept of exterior space around the Universe, whose intrinsic antinomy was pointed by Nicolaus Cusa (1954), Copernicus, Descartes (Koyré, 1962) and others.

The idea of exterior space outside the Universe implies the concept of a Universe limited by a surface separating matter from vacuum, which is a senseless proposition. In fact, space as such, is a set of all possible positions of bodies relative to each others, i.e., a common form of phenomena (Weyl, 1950). As Saint Augustine (1958) remarked, the place of the universe is in itself , and there is no sense in talking about the Cosmos' exterior.

11.2.   Einstein-Mach's Principle - (I)

We saw, in the last Section, the objections that can be raised against Newton's conception of infinite and absolute space, as well as the contradictory character of a cosmology based in his gravitational theory. Ernst Mach (1912), at the end of the nineteenth century, saw the difficulty involved in the justification given by Newton to the existence of an absolute reference system independent of the matter field, based on the consideration of local inertial forces. Logically, Mach refuted Newton's conclusion, on grounds that a reference system can only have physical significance, if it is tied to a matter field. He concluded, therefore, that local inertial accelerations should be referred to an inertial cosmic frame, defined by the distant masses of the Universe, which also implied in the existence of a **cosmic time**.

Einstein (1923), considering Mach's criticism, and, taking the causality principle in the definition of forces into account, inferred that local inertial forces are determined by a gravitational interaction between the local system and the distribution of cosmic masses. This is the famous Mach Principle, as coined by Einstein. So, Mach Principle encompasses two fundamental elements, as cited by Brans and Dicke (1961) and Gomide (1973):

1) Local accelerations are related to an inertial cosmic reference system determined by the distribution of the (distant) masses of the Universe.

2) These accelerations, which are responsible for inertial forces, are the result of a gravitational interaction between the local system and the (distant) cosmic masses. Inertial effects are connected with the gravitational interaction.

Mach Principle as formulated by Einstein, requires that the content of the causality principle for the existence of forces can not be justified by a mere appeal to an absolute reference frame, because these forces have their *raison d' être* in the reality of a physical interaction. The explanation given by Newton, as we saw earlier, hurts a fundamental principle of ontology. Einstein's philosophical view is much more penetrating than that of his XVIIth century colleague. Robert Dicke (1967) observes that Einstein succeeded better, when he based his GRT in dense philosophical analyses.

Mach Principle implies that a cosmic reference frame is determined by the distribution of masses in the Universe. Now, relativistic physics shows us that the material processes occur in a four dimensional continuum. By consequence, time must be associated to any frame in the universe. This fundamental notion may induce a more penetrating view of the problem caused by the existence of inertial forces in local reference frames, and to the better understanding of the difference between of the proper time and coordinate time, as referred to Mach Principle.

We repeat now, some paragraphs of Chapter 6.

Given one local reference frame not subject to accelerations we could employ cylindrical coordinates in order to define the usual metric of Special Relativity. Let it be:

$$ d\tilde{s}^2 = -\left[d\tilde{r}^2 + \tilde{r}^2 d\tilde{\phi}^2 + d\tilde{z}^2\right] + c^2 dt^2 \ . \tag{11.2.1} $$

Consider now a rotating frame, such that:

$$ z = \tilde{z} $$
$$ r = \tilde{r} $$
$$ t = \tilde{t} $$
$$ \phi = \tilde{\phi} - \omega t \ . $$

Let ω be the angular velocity, so that the new metric is given by:

$$ ds^2 = -\left[dr^2 + r^2 d\phi^2 + dz^2\right] + 2r^2 \omega d\phi dt + (c^2 - \omega^2 r^2) dt^2 \ . \tag{11.2.2} $$

Consider now two observers at rest in both reference frames, respectively; we shall have:

$$ d\tilde{s}^2 = c^2 dt^2 \ . \tag{11.2.3} $$

$$ ds^2 = (c^2 - \omega^2 r^2) dt^2 \ . \tag{11.2.4} $$

We see that the proper times in both frames are different from one another, and related by:

$$ ds^2 = (c^2 - \omega^2 r^2)(d\tilde{s}^2/c^2) \ . \tag{11.2.4.a} $$

We may infer that the problem which left Newton perplex, i.e., the impossibility of application of the relativity principle from inertial to rotating frames is originated by a property ignored at the time, namely that time is relativistic and not absolute. The duality between proper time and coordinate time is underlined in the grounds of rotating frames and it can be perceived by the privileged character of the frame under centrifugal acceleration; its consequence is the existence of a metric component $g_{00} \neq 1$, and given by:

$$ g_{00} = (c^2 - \omega^2 r^2)/c^2 \ , \tag{11.2.5} $$

between isotropic or anisotropic models of the Universe, in favor of the former; or between homogeneous or inhomogeneous models of the Universe, choosing the former, etc.

Principles of "cosmic time" and "correspondence"

For consistency, we must impose a correspondence law, contained in the statement:

"General Relativity reduces to Special Relativity in the absence of gravitation; it reduces to Newtonian gravitation theory in the case of weak gravitational field and low speeds; and to Newtonian mechanics, in the absence of gravitation, and for low speeds".

By the same token, we do not admit, in General Relativity, variations, either in time or in space, of the constants in the theory:

$$\frac{\partial G}{\partial x^\alpha} = \frac{\partial m_0}{\partial x^\alpha} = \frac{\partial c}{\partial x^\alpha} = \frac{\partial \varepsilon_0}{\partial x^\alpha} = \frac{\partial \mu_0}{\partial x^\alpha} = 0 . \qquad (\ \alpha = 0,1,2,3\ )$$

In the above, G, m_0, c, ε_0, μ_0 are respectively Newton's gravitational constant, rest mass, speed of light, permittivities of electric and magnetic origin (the reader should be acquainted with the usual denomination of the latter, *permeability constant*; I prefer to call it magnetic permittivity, but this denomination, is my own).

Of course, removing the first term requirement makes for Brans-Dicke theory; the second one, for Kaluza-Klein-Wesson penta-dimensional theory; the other three, for Albrecht-Magueijo's. (Brans and Dicke, 1961; Wesson, 1999, 2006; Albrecht and Magueijo, 1998).

Consider the metric line-element:

$$ds^2 = g_{\mu\nu}dx^\mu dx^\nu . \qquad (11.2.10)$$

If the observer is at rest,

$$dx^i = 0 \qquad (\ i = 1,2,3\ ),$$

while,

$$dx^0 = dt . \qquad (11.2.11)$$

This last equality defines a proper time; we called cosmic time, in Cosmology.

From the geodesics' equations, we shall have:

$$\frac{d^2 x^i}{ds^2} + \Gamma^i_{\alpha\beta} \frac{dx^\alpha}{ds} \frac{dx^\beta}{ds} = \Gamma^i_{00} . \qquad (11.2.12)$$

We then find:

$$g^{ij}\frac{\partial g_{i0}}{\partial t} = 0 . \qquad (11.2.13)$$

This defines a Gaussian coordinate system, which in general implies that:

$$\frac{\partial g_{i0}}{\partial t} = 0 .$$

(11.2.14)

We must now reset our clocks, so that, the above condition is universal (valid for all the particles in the Universe), and then our metric will assume the form:

$$ds^2 = dt^2 - g_{ij}(\vec{x},t)\,dx^i dx^j .$$

(11.2.15)

If we further impose that, in the origin of time, we have:

$$g_{i0}(t = 0) = 0 ,$$

(11.2.16)

then by (11.2.14), we shall have:

$$g_{i0}(t) = 0 .$$

(11.2.17)

The above defines a Gaussian normal coordinate system.

For a comoving observer, in a freely falling perfect fluid, the quadrivelocity u^μ will obey:

$$u^i = 0 ,$$

(11.2.18)

while, if we normalize the quadrivelocity, we find, from the condition:

$$g_{\mu\nu} u^\mu u^\nu = 1 ,$$

(11.2.19)

that,

$$g_{00} u^0 = 1 .$$

(11.2.20)

Though Gomide and Berman (1988) have discussed the case $g_{00} = g_{00}(t) \neq 1$, we usually impose:

$$g_{00} = u^0 = 1 .$$

(11.2.21)

The purpose we have in mind, is to define a Machian metric; Gaussian coordinate systems, in fact, imply that, with $g_{0i} = 0$, there are no rotations in the metric (we refer to formula (11.2.3) to the contrary), and in each point we may define a locally inertial reference system.

Gaussian normal coordinates were called "synchronous" ; in an arbitrary spacetime, when we pick a spacelike hypersurface S_0 , and we eject geodesic lines orthogonal to it, with constant coordinates x^1, x^2 and x^3 , while $x^0 \equiv t + t_0$, where $t_0 = 0$ on S_0, then t is the proper time, whose origin is $t = 0$ on S_0 (see MTW, 1973) .

In the above treatment, cosmic time is, relativistically speaking, "absolute", so that the measure of the age of the Universe, according to this "time", is not "relative".

Picture #1: "Classical" viewpoint

Either the body is free-falling towards the Sun, or it is the Sun that falls towards it. In the former case, the body free-falls towards the Sun, but suffers an acceleration towards the distant fixed masses; in the latter, both the Sun and the distant masses, do accelerate towards the "fixed" (at rest) body.

Picture #2: "Sciama-Mach's" viewpoint

When we consider the earlier picture, the rest body feels a gravitational force from the Sun, and is *inertially* (accelerated) by the distant masses. The inertia property, is originated by a gravitational interaction. Sciama also expects, that there could be found a special zero-total force coordinate system, under which, a) inertial force is balanced by the Sun's gravitational force, so that, the sum of all forces is equal to zero; b) as in electrodynamics, because accelerations means radiation, it is distant matter, because it is accelerated, that radiates (read, *gravitons*); c) it is this radiation, which causes the *inertia* , on the body. This radiation, as well as in electrodynamics, is time-retarded, and, thus, the inertial property falls with the inverse of radial distance, i.e., with r^{-1} ; d) the inertial force F_i , caused by the distant masses (total mass M), with acceleration a , on a body of mass m , is given by, in analogy with electrodynamics,

$F_i = \frac{GMma}{rc^2}$; e) it is the fact that $M \neq 0$, which causes the force F_i ; if those fixed stars, were not there, F_i would be zero; inertia would result, according to the above, from the interaction of the local body's mass with the total mass distribution in the Universe; f) inertia has the simple formulation described above, in the special coordinate system where the sum of forces, i.e., the total force on the body equals zero, i.e., $\vec{F}_{grav} + \vec{F}_i = 0$.

A problem with the above theory, is that it is not coordinate-independent. Differently than in Sciama's case, Synge (1960) tells that spacetime is endowed with specific Physical properties; than motions would proceed through this specific spacetime. In GRT, flat spacetime, due to the fact that the absence of distant masses would not forbid the existence of inertial mass on a given body, we can cite that even Schwarzschild's metric, where boundary conditions at infinity are Minkowski's, does not forbid inertia (i.e., the inertial mass is still there).

11.5.   Scalar Fields and Machian Properties

In Section 11.3, we exposed Dicke's ideas on the necessity for a tensor gravitational potential. Now, we analyze a possible auxiliary scalar field, that could be incorporated into gravitational theories.

Five points must be remembered:

1- GRT is a particular case for gravitational theories, whose only cause resides in a tensor. This tensor is composed of the metric coefficients of a Riemannian geometry, attached to spacetime.

2- Spacetime geometry is **absolute.** GRT is not necessarily Machian *avant la lettre* .

3- Linearized gravitation is analogous to electrodynamics (Sciama's theory, which is indeed Machian).

4- Non-linear gravitation, like GRT, could be made "Machian", by introducing a new tensor field. However, if this tensor field is a new one, it might be expected that it could lead to anisotropies in spacetime, for instance, in the vacuum. In a reference frame, with locally Minkowskian metric, either we would find anisotropies, or, else, both tensor fields, the metric and the new one, would be one and the same.

5- In #4 , we might try to move, from one point of spacetime to other point, in order to check that it would be not a coincidence, that, it was only in a particular point, where the two tensors coincided.

Alternatively, we may introduce a new field, this time, a *scalar* one. In this case, we obtain *scalar-tensor theories*. A soft introduction to such theories, in their cosmological face, can be found in the book by Berman (2007a). The first theory of this kind, is BD gravitation (Brans and Dicke, 1961).

In the remainder of this Section, we shall, first, comment about the interesting properties we should expect from the scalar field to be introduced, and next, we shall mathematize our analysis (Dicke, 1964, 1964a).

Call the scalar field as ϕ .

$\rightarrow$ It has two result in attractive forces; weak ones; its range, compatible with the gravitational interaction;

$\rightarrow$ it should not affect light's propagation with speed c ;

$\rightarrow$ for speeds v , it should decrease as speeds increase, so as to end into a null modification, when $v = c$ (why would we not try, say, for instance, $\phi = \phi_0 \sqrt{1 - v^2/c^2}$?);

$\rightarrow$ the gravitational interaction must be related to the scalar field, through their masses;

$\rightarrow$ this scalar field must be universal, and affect all masses with the same factor, or else the Eötvös experimental evidence on the free-fall being equivalent for two different materials.

Then, we must find a time-varying gravitational "constant" . Thus, we require that proper times read by clocks, and proper lengths, as measured by rods, should not differ from one point of space to the other. [We refer the reader, to Section 13.1 below and to Section 11.3 above.]

We now go to a mathematical treatment of ϕ .

Consider the scalar field, as tied to a matter field, and coordinate-dependent (i.e., varying with $x^i \equiv x^0, x^1, x^2, x^3$). The associated four-force, is given by:

$$F_i = \frac{\partial \phi}{\partial x^i} .$$

(11.5.1)

Chapter 12

The Zero-Total-Energy of the Machian Universe

12.1. Brans-Dicke-Sciama-Whitrow-Randall's Relation

Brans-Dicke relation (Weinberg, 1972; Brans and Dicke, 1961; Whitrow, 1946; Whitrow and Randall, 1951; Sciama, 1953), also attributed earlier to Whitrow, Randall and Sciama, consists in the amazing relation:

$$\frac{GM}{c^2 R} \sim 1 \qquad\qquad (12.1.1)$$

where, M refers to the mass of a "large" sphere (containing the finite mass of the causally related Universe, i.e. in the Hubble's radius), and R is the radius of the boundary of the Universe represented by such sphere. This relation is obeyed quite exactly, when we plug in it the data for the mass and radius estimated for the known Universe. This relation was the basis for the implementation of Brans-Dicke theory, in contradistinction with GRT. It has been suggested that G needs to be time-varying in order that the above relation may prevail for the Universe.

A rough evidence for Brans-Dicke relation is the known result that the energy of the Universe is zero (see for instance, Berman, 2005; 2005 b). In the last two references, it is shown, that according to GRT, the energy contents of a sphere like the above one, is given by (Adler et al., 1975):

$$E = Mc^2 - \frac{GM^2}{2R} = 0 , \qquad\qquad (12.1.2)$$

where the first term in rhs represents the inertial part of the energy, while the second term in the rhs represents the gravitational potential or self energy of the distribution. Then, with $E = 0$ we find $\frac{GM}{2c^2 R} = 1$. In order that the latter relation be applied to the whole Universe, we substitute it by the so-called Brans-Dicke relation (12.1.1) :

$$\frac{GM}{c^2 R} \sim 1 \qquad\qquad (12.1.1)$$

12.3.   Energy of the Universe and Mach's Principle

We now shall propose that Mach's Principle, means a zero-total energy Universe. (Feynman, 1962-1963; Berman, 2006; 2006a), have shown this meaning of Mach's Principle without considering a rotating Universe. We now extend the model, in order to include the spin of the Universe, and we replace Brans-Dicke traditional relation, $\frac{GM}{c^2R} \sim 1$, with three different relations, which we call the Brans-Dicke relations for gravitation, for the cosmological "constant" , and for the spin of the Universe.

We shall consider a "large" sphere, with mass M , radius R , spin L , and endowed with a cosmological term Λ , which causes the existence of an energy density $\frac{\Lambda}{\kappa}$, where $\kappa = \frac{8\pi G}{c^2}$. We now calculate the total energy E of this distribution:

$$E = E_i + E_g + E_L + E_\Lambda, \tag{12.3.1}$$

where $E_i = Mc^2$, stands for the inertial (Special Relativistic) energy; $E_g \cong -\frac{GM^2}{R}$ (the Newtonian gravitational potential self-energy); $E_L \cong \frac{L^2}{MR^2}$ the Newtonian rotational energy; and $E_\Lambda \cong \frac{\Lambda R^3}{6G}$ (the cosmological "constant" energy contained within the sphere).

If we impose that the total energy is equal to zero, i.e., $E = 0$, we obtain from (12.3.1):

$$\frac{GM}{c^2R} - \frac{L^2}{M^2c^2R^2} - \frac{\Lambda R^3}{6GMc^2} \cong 1. \tag{12.3.2}$$

As relation(12.3.2) above should be valid for the whole Universe, and not only for a specific instant of time, in the life of the Universe, and if this is not a coincidental relation, we can solve this equation by imposing that:

$$\frac{GM}{c^2R} = \gamma_G \sim 1 , \tag{12.3.3}$$

$$\frac{L}{McR} = \gamma_L \sim 1, \tag{12.3.4}$$

and,

$$\frac{\Lambda R^3}{6GMc^2} = \gamma_\Lambda \sim 1, \tag{12.3.5}$$

subject to the condition,

$$\gamma_G - \gamma_L^2 - \gamma_\Lambda \sim 1, \tag{12.3.6}$$

where the $\gamma's$ are constants having a near unity value.

We now propose the following generalized Brans-Dicke relations, for gravitation, spin and cosmological "constant":

$$\frac{GM}{c^2R} = \gamma_G \sim 1 , \tag{12.3.3}$$

$$\frac{GL}{c^3R^2} = \gamma_G \cdot \gamma_L \sim 1, \tag{12.3.7}$$

and,

$$\frac{\Lambda R^2}{6c^4} = \gamma_\Lambda \cdot \gamma_G \sim 1. \tag{12.3.8}$$

The reader should note that we have termed Λ as a "constant", but it is clear from the above, that in an expanding Universe, $\Lambda \propto R^{-2}$, so that Λ is a variable term. We also notice that $R \propto M$, and $L \propto R^2$.

The B.D. relation for spin, has been derived, on a heuristic procedure, which consists on the simple hypothesis that L should obey a similar relation as M (Sabbata and Sivaram, 1994). The first authors to propose the above R^{-2} dependence for Λ were Chen and Wu (1990), under the hypothesis that Λ should not depend on Planck's constant, because the cosmological "constant" is the Classical Physics response to otherwise Quantum effects that originated the initial energy of the vacuum. Berman, as well as Berman and Som, have examined, along with other authors, a time dependence for Λ(see for example, Berman, 1991; 1991a).

It must be remarked, that our proposed law (12.3.3), is a radical departure from the original Brans-Dicke (Brans and Dicke, 1961) relation, which was an approximate one, while our present hypothesis implies that $R \propto M$. With the present hypothesis, one can show that, independently of the particular gravitational theory taken as valid, the energy densities of the Machian Universe obey a R^{-2} dependence (see Berman, 2006; 2006a; Berman and Marinho, 2001).

Consider, for instance, the inertial energy density. We define,

$$\rho = \frac{M}{V}, \tag{12.3.9}$$

while,

$$V = \alpha R^3, \quad (\alpha = \text{constant}) \tag{12.3.10}$$

where ρ and V stand for energy density and tridimensional volume, we find:

$$\rho = \left[\frac{\gamma_G}{G\alpha}\right] R^{-2}. \tag{12.3.11}$$

For all other kinds of energy densitites (gravitational, lambda, or spin-originated), we also find the R^{-2} dependence, when we admit the above Brans-Dicke generalised relations, as the reader may easily check

If we apply the above relation, for Planck's and the present Universe, we find:

$$\frac{\rho}{\rho_{Pl}} = \left[\frac{R}{R_{Pl}}\right]^{-2}. \tag{12.3.12}$$

If we substitute the known values for Planck's quantities, while we take for the present Universe, $R \cong 10^{28}$ cm, we find a reasonable result for the present energy density. This shows that our result (relation 12.3.11), has to be given credit.

It should be remembered that the origin of Planck's quantities, say, for length, time, density and mass, were obtained by means of dimensional combinations among the constants for macrophysics (G for gravitation and c for electromagnetism) and for Quantum Physics (Planck's constant $\frac{h}{2\pi}$). Analogously, if we would demand a dimensionally correct Planck's spin, obviously we would find,

$$L_{Pl} = \frac{h}{2\pi} . \tag{12.3.13}$$

From Brans-Dicke relation for spin, we now can obtain the present angular momentum of the Universe,

$$L = L_{Pl} \left[\frac{R}{R_{Pl}} \right]^2 \cong 10^{120} \left(\frac{h}{2\pi} \right) = 10^{93} \quad g \ cm^2 \ s^{-1} . \tag{12.3.14}$$

This estimate was also made by Sabbata and Sivaram(1994), based on heuristic considerations(see also Sabbata and Gasperini, 1979).

If we employ, for the cosmological "constant" Planck's value, Λ_{Pl} ,

$$\Lambda_{Pl} \cong R_{Pl}^{-2} , \tag{12.3.15}$$

then, we shall find, in close agreement with the present value estimate for Λ (as found by recent supernovae observations), by means of the third Brans-Dicke relation:

$$\Lambda = \Lambda_{Pl} \left[\frac{R_{Pl}}{R} \right]^{-2} . \tag{12.3.16}$$

We refer to analysis in Section 12.6, in order to check that, corresponding the equation $E = 0$,which applies to the zero-total energy of the Universe, we also find $\bar{\rho} = 0$, i.e., the effective energy density of the Universe is also zero ($\bar{\rho} = \frac{dE}{dV} = 0$), where V represents volume. Thus, as these results are time-invariant, we assert that they are valid at time $t = 0$. Such being the case, we conclude that in the Machian Universe, there is no room for the so-called initial singularity (infinite total energy density at initial time).

12.4. Application 1: Angular Velocity of the Universe and Pioneer Anomaly

Sabbata and Gasperini(1979), have calculated the angular speed of the Universe, for the present Universe. Though they mixed their calculations with some results obtained from Dirac's LNH (Large Number Hypothesis), including a time variation for the gravitational "constant", we now show that, if we take for granted that $G = $ constant, and by means of the generalized Brans-Dicke relations we find, by considering a rigid rotating Universe, whereby:

For Planck's Universe, we would have, with $R_{Pl} \cong 10^{-33}$ cm,

$$B_{Pl} = B\left[\frac{R}{R_{Pl}}\right] \cong 10^{55} \text{ Gauss.}$$

This last value is larger than the maximum limit for the magnetic field not to provoke instabilities in the vacuum, according to a recent analysis made through Quantum Electrodynamics theory (QED), by Shabad and Usov(2006). That being the case, we can imagine this fact as causing the eruption of the inflationary phase, mediately after Planck's time.

We have derived the dependency of the magnetic field with R^{-1}, from the zero-total energy conjecture, in a Machian Universe, (see relation 12.5.4 above),obtaining a result valid during the lifespan of the Universe.

We remark that Sabbata and Sivaram(1994) obtained for the Planck's magnetic field, $B'_{pl} \sim 10^{58}$ Gauss, which is larger than in our estimate. But the law of variation of the magnetic field, with the age of the Universe, is our own.

12.6. Application 3: Time-Varying Neutrino Mass

The subject of mass-varying neutrinos, has been very recently given attention (Horvat, 2005; Fardon et al, 2003; Kaplan, 2004). Berman (2007; 2007a) has made, with the help of F.M. Gomide, an historical review of the neutrino research and considered its rôle as dark matter in the Universe. It has been asserted, that 67% of the energy density of the Universe, is due to a cosmological "constant" energy. The rest of the energy density is fractionated in two parts: 5% as visible mass and 28% as dark matter. Let us suppose that dark matter is constituted by neutrinos with non-zero rest mass. Berman(2006, 2006a, 2006b)has suggested that, if Mach's principle is understood as meaning that the total energy of the Universe is null, and if each particular energy contribution to the total energy density, has constant participation during the whole history of the Universe, one may obtain different Machian relations. These Machian relations, of which, the Brans-Dicke (Brans and Dicke, 1961) relation is a particular case, should not, according to Berman, be viewed as just coincidental with the present Universe.

Suppose that the total energy is given by:

$$E = Mc^2 - \frac{GM^2}{2R} + 4\pi\Lambda\frac{R^3}{3\kappa} + \frac{L^2}{MR^2}, \tag{12.6.1}$$

where the four terms to the right of relation (12.6.1) represent respectively the inertial, gravitational, cosmological constant's and rotational energies.

When we impose,

$$E = 0, \tag{12.6.2}$$

we obtain the generalised Brans-Dicke relations of Section 12.3, which are: (12.3.3), (12.3.4), (12.3.5) and (12.3.6). Then, we can check that all energy densities are proportional to R^{-2}, so that, we can also write:

$$L = MR^2\omega, \tag{12.4.1}$$

so that,

$M\omega = $ constant , (because $L \propto R^2$ as we have shown earlier), we shall have:

$$\omega_{Pl} = \frac{c}{R_{Pl}} = 2 \times 10^{43} \ s^{-1}, \tag{12.4.2}$$

and, for the present,

$$\omega = \frac{c}{R} \cong 3 \times 10^{-18} \ s^{-1}. \tag{12.4.3}$$

It must be pointed out, that the result (12.4.2) seems to us that was not published elsewhere, up to now. This is, however, the first time that the above results are obtained by means of the zero-total energy hypothesis for the Universe. This is why we attribute this hypothesis to a Machian Universe; indeed, we believe that we can identify Mach's Principle, with this hypothesis.

Sabbata and Gasperini(1979), pointed out that the same numerical angular speed is obtained for Gödel's Universe, and also for the Sun's peculiar velocity through the cosmic microwave background.

We remark that $\gamma_G \cong 2$ is to be exact and not approximate, if we consider the result by Adler et al (1975), for the energy of a spherical mass, obtained by means of pseudotensors.

The Pioneers' anomaly, is described by a centripetal acceleration of an up to now unexplained nature, which affects two spaceships launched on opposite directions, which are by now in the outskirts of the Solar system. Its value is $a' \cong -8 \times 10^{-8} cm/\sec^2$.

For a Machian Universe, taken care of result (12.3.11),we can obtain the value for an ubiquitous centripetal acceleration,

$$a = -\omega^2 R. \tag{12.4.4}$$

If $R \cong 10^{28} cm$, as is known for the causally related Universe, we find:

$$a = -9 \times 10^{-8} cm/\sec^2 \cong a'. \tag{12.4.5}$$

It is necessary to point out that, for a Machian Universe, we should have this extra acceleration, along the direction pointing from the observed to the observer. It affects any two pairs of, observer versus observed, points in space. The striking match between a and a' must point to a possible solution to the Pioneers' anomaly; the only necessary hypothesis is that the Universe is endowed with the Machian properties shown above.

12.5. Application 2: Magnetic Field of the Universe

In two recent chapters of books (Berman, 2006; 2006a) has proposed a new interpretation for Brans-Dicke relation, which, instead of being an approximate relation only valid for the present Universe, should be interpreted as meaning that the mass M , of the causally related Universe, is directly proportional to the radius R , in the entire life of the Universe. In the same references, it is shown that, the new interpretation of Brans-Dicke relation, along with the hypothesis that the cosmological "constant" varies with R^{-2}, arise from the imposition that the total energy of the Universe, is zero-valued. Sabbata and Sivaram(1994), have shown that, in analogy with Brans-Dicke approximate relation, one could state another similar one for the spin of the Universe L. Again, Berman(2006a), extending his conjectures on the zero-total energy of the Universe, and including in the total energy, a term representing the rotational energy, derived Sabbata and Sivaram(1994) relation, as an exact formula, indicating that L varied with R^2 during all times. In all cases, Berman has made the hypothesis, that the fraction of each kind of energy participation, did not vary with time, when taken as fractions of Mc^2.

We now extend Berman's hypotheses, while keeping a new term which contributes to the total energy of the Universe, dictated by the magnetic field. The fraction of magnetic energy participation to the total energy, is nevertheless kept in a 10^{-3} orders of magnitude, because we take for granted that the observed equipartition between the microwave background radiation, and magnetic field energies, for interstellar media, point out to a similar fraction in the magnetic field of the Universe. We impose that such fraction endures for the entire history of the Universe; in fact, this means that we adjust our Machian relation for the magnetic field, in order that its present value should be around 10^{-6} Gauss.

As the fractions of energy, of any kind, in the Machian Universe, according to our theory, are to be maintained, we take for granted, that any kind of energy's density, vary with R^{-2}, as has been shown, for the total energy density, by Berman(2006; 2006a) and Berman and Marinho Jr(2001). For each type of energy, we would have a constant fraction of the total energy, i.e., constant in time. For the inertial energy density, we would have:

$$\rho = \frac{M}{\frac{4}{3}\pi R^3}. \tag{12.5.1}$$

From Brans-Dicke relation, as modified by Berman, we have:

$$\frac{GM}{Rc^2} = \gamma = \text{ constant } \sim 1. \tag{12.5.2}$$

From (12.5.1) and (12.5.2), we obtain the desired dependence, $\rho \propto R^{-2}$.

The energy density associated with a magnetic field B is given by:

$$\rho_B = \frac{B^2}{8\pi}. \tag{12.5.3}$$

In mass units, we have to divide the second member of (12.5.3) by c^2. The total energy fraction for the magnetic field, relative to Mc^2 would be given by:

$$\left[\frac{4}{3}\pi R^3\right]\left[\frac{B^2}{8\pi c^2}\right]\left[Mc^2\right]^{-1} = \gamma_B \cong 10^{-6}. \tag{12.5.4}$$

We then find that $B \propto R^{-1}$ because, in fact, from (12.5.4) we have:

$$B^2 = 12 \; c^4 \, \gamma \, \gamma_B \, G^{-1} R^{-2}. \tag{12.5.5}$$

We then find, for the present Universe, with $R \cong 10^{28}$ cm, $B \cong 10^{-6}$ Gauss .

$$\rho_{TOT} = \rho_1 + \rho_2 + \rho_3 = \Gamma R^{-2} \quad (\; \Gamma = \text{constant} \;). \tag{12.6.3}$$

Let us obtain the self gravitational energy density:

It can not be forgotten that zero-total energy, means also zero-total energy density. However, we call the effective total energy density as

$$\bar{\rho} = \rho_{TOT} + \rho_{grav} = -\frac{Mc^2}{\frac{4}{3}\pi R^3} + \Gamma R^{-2} = 0, \tag{12.6.4}$$

[where ρ_{grav} is the (negative) gravitational self-energy density correspondent to the self-gravitational energy, ($E_{grav} \cong -\frac{G\,M^2}{2R}$) which is representative of the total energy of the Schwarzschild's metric - see relation (12.6.1)].

$$\rho_{grav} = \frac{dE_{grav}}{dV} = \frac{1}{4\pi R^2}\left[\frac{dE_{grav}}{dR}\right] = -\frac{2c^4\gamma_1^2}{4\pi GR^2}\frac{dR}{dR} = -\frac{2c^4\gamma_1^2}{4\pi G}R^{-2}$$

The constant $\Gamma > 0$ is adjusted accordingly. What we call the energy density of the Universe, is in fact ρ_{TOT}.

The effective total energy density, $\bar{\rho} = 0$, is to be coherent with zero-total energy. This is obtained by adding both total energy densities above, i.e.,

$$\bar{\rho} = \rho_{grav} + \rho_{TOT} = \Gamma' R^{-2} + \Gamma R^{-2} = 0.$$

We see that,

$$\Gamma' + \Gamma = 0.$$

In the spirit of inflationary Cosmology (Guth, 1981), we identify, for the present Universe, ρ_{TOT} with the critical density, so that we would have:

$$\rho_{TOT} \cong 2 \text{ x } 10^{-29} \text{ g / cm}^3 .$$

In the next few paragraphs, we estimate neutrinos average mass, and its time variation. But, we observe that, if dark matter is a fraction of ρ_{TOT}, this fraction will also depend on R^{-2}, so as to keep all relative components equally balanced along time.

A theory for neutrinos energy density

As we have noticed before the energy density of dark matter, to be identified with neutrinos, shall be given by:

$$\rho_\nu = 0.27\rho_{TOT} . \tag{12.6.5}$$

Berman (2006c) along with others (see Sabbata and Sivaram, 1994) have estimated that the Universe possess a magnetic field which, for Planck's Universe, was as huge as 10^{55} Gauss. The relic magnetic field of the present Universe is estimated in 10^{-6} Gauss. We can then, suppose that all neutrinos' spins have been aligned with the magnetic field. On the other hand, the spin of the Universe is believed to have increased in accordance with Machian relations(12.3.3) to (12.3.8), which entails that $L \propto R^2$. If we call n the number of neutrinos in the present Universe, and n_{Pl} its value for Planck's Universe, we may write:

$$\frac{n}{n_{Pl}} = \frac{L}{L_{Pl}} = 10^{120}.$$
(12.6.6)

Then,

$$n = n_{Pl} \left[\frac{R}{R_{Pl}} \right]^2 .$$
(12.6.7)

We have just obtained the relation for the increase of the number of neutrinos with R^2.

Now, we write the energy density of neutrinos,

$$\rho_v \cong \frac{n m_v}{\frac{4}{3}\pi R^3},$$
(12.6.8)

where m_v is the rest mass of the average neutrino.

If we impose relation (12.6.5) and simultaneously, relations (12.6.3) and (12.6.8), we conclude two things:

1st.) $\rho_v = 0.27 \rho_{Pl} \left[\frac{R}{R_{Pl}} \right]^{-2}.$
(12.6.9)

2nd.) $m_v = \frac{\rho_{Pl} R_{Pl}^4}{R}.$

We see now that while the number of neutrinos in the Universe increases with R^2 , the rest mass decreases with R^{-1} ; we may obtain, with $R \cong 10^{28}$ cm, that the rest mass of neutrinos should be, in the present Universe:

$$m_v \cong 10^{-65} \text{ g.}$$
(12.6.10)

F.M. Gomide (1963), has estimated the mass of neutrinos a long time ago, finding, in a seminal paper , the value, 10^{-65} g. One of the two different arguments by Gomide (Gomide, 1963), was in fact that he equated $m_v c^2$ with the self-gravitational energy of the proton.

A law of variation for the number of neutrinos in the Universe has been found. A law of variation for the rest mass of neutrinos was also found.

One can check, that the microlength for the present Universe represents a quantum, which we call the present Universe's value for the *somium*. Macrolength is represented by the radius of the Universe.

For Planck's Universe, the *somium* coincides with Planck's length; both macro and micro, then coincide with the Planck's radius.

We have found that the micromass and microlength represent quanta of mass and length. We call them, respectively, *gomidium* and *somium*, but their numerical values are time-varying: present day's *gomidium* is 10^{-65} g, while *somium* is about 10^{-91} cm. Planck's values for *gomidium* and *somium*, are respectively given by Planck's mass and Planck's length. We have thus hinted that mass is quantized, but geometry is altogether. As gravitation is associated with geometry, quantization of the latter, implies on the former: it seems that quantum gravity has been found.

Removal of initial singularity in Cosmology

From what has been dealt before, in this Section, it follows that, the initial singularity of the Universe, is now deleted from our Machian Universe picture: as the effective energy density $\bar{\rho} = 0$, and the total energy of the Universe $E = 0$, we have not to deal with infinities while calculating those quantities in the limit $R \to 0$.

12.8. Entropy of Black Holes and Machian Universes

For a Reissner-Nordström's black hole, we have seen in Section 10.2 that the energy density is given by,

$$\rho = AR_S^{-2}. \ (\ A = \text{constant}\ ) \tag{12.8.1}$$

The above result, is of course, true, for $Q = 0$ and, the Schwarzschild's radius $R = R_S = 2M_{bh}$.

On the other hand, if a black hole has $Q \neq 0$, we may write,

$$Q^2 = \alpha M^2. \ (\ \alpha = \text{constant}\ ) \tag{12.8.2}$$

Then, a relation of the type (12.8.1), would also apply.

If the black hole, even in a Classical Thermodynamical picture, is seen as a black body, its energy density would be given, in terms of the absolute temperature T_{bh}, by,

$$\rho_r = \sigma T^4. \ (\ \sigma = \text{constant}\ ) \tag{12.8.3}$$

When, one equates (12.8.1) and (12.8.3), we find that,

$$R_S T^2 = \sqrt{\tfrac{A}{\sigma}} = \text{constant}.$$

From any book on thermodynamics, (see, for instance, Sears and Salinger, 1975), we find that the entropy of this black body thermodynamical entity is given by:

$$S_{bh} = \tfrac{16}{9}\pi\sigma R_S^3 T_{bh}^3.$$
(12.8.5)

In terms of either, the Schwarzschild's radius, R_S, or in terms of T, due to the relation (12.8.4), we may write:

$$S_{bh} = \tfrac{16}{9}\pi\sigma \left[\sqrt{\tfrac{A}{\sigma}}\right]^{-3/2} R_S^{3/2} = \tfrac{16}{9}\pi\sigma \left[\sqrt{\tfrac{A}{\sigma}}\right]^3 T_{bh}^{-3}.$$
(12.8.6)

Now, consider a Machian Universe. We have seen that for this Machian property, i.e., the zero-total energy property, all energy densities decrease with R_U^{-2}. If the Universe itself resembles a black body, we would found, as in the similar case of black holes, that, by equating the energy density, ρ_U, with the radiation energy, ρ_r, given by:

$$\rho_U = A R_U^{-2} = \sigma T_U^4 = \rho_r,$$
(12.8.7)

we find a relation similar to (12.8.4), provided that we change, from R_S and T_{bh}, into R_U and T_U. We would keep the same formula, in both cases, for the entropy of the Universe or black holes:

$$S_U = \tfrac{16}{9}\pi\sigma \left[\sqrt{\tfrac{A}{\sigma}}\right]^{-3/2} R_U^{3/2} = \tfrac{16}{9}\pi\sigma \left[\sqrt{\tfrac{A}{\sigma}}\right]^3 T_U^{-3}.$$
(12.8.8)

The entropy of the Universe, could be calculated independently, by dividing the total energy, by the temperature,

$$S_U = \tfrac{1}{T_U}\left[\tfrac{4}{3}\pi R_U^3 \rho_U\right] = \tfrac{4}{3}\pi R_U^3 A R_U^{-2}\tfrac{1}{T_U},$$
(12.8.9)

which is equivalent to (12.8.8).

It must be said that the Universe has increasing entropy, because it is expanding; as far as the black hole is clothed, i.e., has a kind of frozen radius R_S, its entropy remains locally constant; if we remember the global expansion effect, of course, its entropy increases likewise. The case of a naked singularity, would be treated as a normal physical situation, according to the treatment given to, say, a contracting star (gravitational collapse).

For a black hole, the only way for the entropy to increase, if it is clothed, would be by accreting matter from its neighborhood, or by coalescing with other bodies.

Chapter 13

Alternative Machian Gravitational Theories

13.1.   Brans-Dicke and Scalar Tensor Theories

Generalized Large Number Hypothesis

This Section extends ideas due to the Nobel Prize winner Paul Adrien Maurice Dirac (Berman, 1994; Dirac, 1938; Eddington, 1935). When we divide Hubble's length, cH_0^{-1} by the Classical Electron's radius, $\frac{e^2}{m_e c^2}$, we find the non-dimensional number 10^{40} :

$$\frac{cH_0^{-1}}{\frac{e^2}{m_e c^2}} \sim 10^{40} .\tag{13.1.1}$$

This same order of magnitude appears when we divide the values for the electrostatic and the gravitational forces between an electron and a proton:

$$\frac{e^2}{G m_p m_e} \sim 10^{40} .\tag{13.1.2}$$

On the other hand, its square, 10^{80} is roughly found for the total number of nucleons in the Universe, which we obtain by multiplying the estimated mass density of the Universe by the cube of Hubble's length and then divide by the proton's mass:

$$\frac{\rho_0 \left(c H_0^{-1} \right)^3}{m_p} \sim (10^{40})^2 = 10^{80} .\tag{13.1.3}$$

The brilliant Paul Dirac established his LNH (large numbers hypothesis) which says that those three numbers are large and not only coincidental: in fact, he said that the numbers are very large because the Universe is old, and they in fact are time-varying and they increase with the age of the Universe so that, in the very early Universe these numbers were smaller. Lord Eddington (1935) found an other large number 10^{40} , verbi gratia:

$$ch(m_p m_e / \Lambda_0)^{1/2} \sim 10^{40},\tag{13.1.4}$$

13.2. Whitrow-Randall's Relation in GRT and B.D. Cosmologies

We refer the reader, before going through this Section, to review Section 12.1. Berman and Som (1990) have commented that a proper theory of gravitation incorporating Brans-Dicke relation, should either account for a constant ratio $\frac{M}{R}$, or allow for a variable G . As the absolute scale of the elementary particle masses can be availed only by measuring gravitational accelerations, it would be more feasible to treat G as variable. Since the interactions are long range, it ought to be related to the average value of a scalar-field ϕ which is coupled to the mass density of the Universe. There is an extensive literature on cosmological models in scalar tensor theories. In this Section we present cosmological models according to B.D. theory that satisfy exactly the Whitrow-Randall's relation. In obtaining these models, we shall look for a solution of the constant deceleration parameter kind, putting

$$q = m - 1. \tag{13.2.1}$$

where q is the (constant) deceleration parameter, and the scale-factor is given by (Berman, 1983; Berman and Gomide, 1988; Gomide and Berman, 1988):

$$R(t) = (mDt)^{1/m} , \tag{13.2.2}$$

where m and D are non-null constants, and Hubble's parameter H is then given by:

$$H \equiv \frac{\dot{R}}{R} = \frac{1}{mt} \tag{13.2.3}$$

We recall now Brans-Dicke cosmological equations in the Robertson-Walker's line element, for a perfect fluid,

$$ds^2 = dt^2 - \frac{R(t)^2}{\left(1+\frac{kr^2}{4}\right)^2} d\sigma^2 ,$$

where,

$$d\sigma^2 = dx^2 + dy^2 + dz^2,$$

we find,

$$\frac{d}{dt}(\dot{\phi}R^3) = \frac{8\pi}{3+2\omega}(\rho - 3p)R^3 \tag{13.2.4}$$

$$\left(\frac{\dot{R}}{R}\right)^2 + \frac{k}{R^2} = \frac{8\pi\rho}{3\phi} - \frac{\dot{\phi}}{\phi}\frac{\dot{R}}{R} + \frac{\omega}{6}\left(\frac{\dot{\phi}}{\phi}\right)^2 \tag{13.2.5}$$

$$\dot{\rho} = -3\frac{\dot{R}}{R}(\rho + p) \tag{13.2.6}$$

$$G - (a\phi)^{-1} - \left(\frac{2\omega+4}{2\omega+3}\right)\phi^{-1} \tag{13.2.7}$$

(13.2.6) is the conservation of energy momentum tensor; (13.2.7) represents the compatibility necessary in order to adjust for the solar results for Brans-Dicke theory; $a > 0$ is also imposed, so that we have the correct deflection of the light path around a gravitational mass. We take Whitrow and Randall's relation, in the following equivalent form:

$$\tfrac{4}{3}\pi G\rho \sim t^{-2} \tag{13.2.8}$$

We shall take, following Berman and Som (1990), the above approximate relation, as exact [see however, next Section, for the exact relation, according to the field equations], and first of all we take $k = 0$ (Euclidean solution); if we plug in the above field equations, relation

$$\rho = \tfrac{3}{4\pi G}t^{-2} \tag{13.2.9}$$

one obtains from (13.2.5) and for $q = \text{constant} = m - 1$,

$$\tfrac{1}{m^2}t^{-2} + \tfrac{\dot{\phi}}{\phi m}t^{-1} - \tfrac{\omega}{6}\tfrac{\dot{\phi}^2}{\phi^2} = 2at^{-2} \tag{13.2.10}$$

The above can be solved by:

$$\phi = At , \tag{13.2.11}$$

provided that:

$$2a = \tfrac{1}{m^2} + \tfrac{1}{m} - \tfrac{\omega}{6} , \tag{13.2.12}$$

which implies that:

$$\left(\omega^2 + 14\omega + 18\right)m^2 = 6(\omega + 2)(1 + m) \tag{13.2.13}$$

From the energy conservation equation, we find:

$$p = C\left(\tfrac{m}{3} - 1\right)t^{-1} \qquad (C = \text{constant}) \tag{13.2.14}$$

From the earlier equations, we now check that energy density ρ and cosmic pressure p are related by a perfect gas equation of state:

$$p = \alpha\rho = \tfrac{m}{3} - 1. \tag{13.2.15}$$

We now apply the above results to the first field equation, (13.2.4), obtaining:

$$\omega + 2 = m(4 - m) . \tag{13.2.16}$$

Since $\omega \neq -2$, we shall have $m \neq 0$ and also $m \neq 4$. Relations (13.2.16) and (13.2.13) yield (Beesham, 1995):

$$m^5 - 8m^4 + 6m^3 + 46m^2 - 24m - 24 = 0. \tag{13.2.17}$$

For each root of equation (13.2.17), corresponds one value for ω, according to (13.2.16).

The positive value for ω is only one:

$$\omega \cong 1.10$$

$$m \cong 1.05$$

This model is a particular case of a general class presented by Morganstern (1971). However, it is our case that obeys Whitrow-Randall's relation exactly. It is the attribute of q = constant models for this case.

Beesham (1995) proposed other solutions to the same problem in the $k = 0$ case yielding q = constant which generalized the solution above. Instead of solution $\phi = At$ (13.2.11), he found a more general one,

$$\phi = Et^F$$

where E, F are constants. We refer to his paper for details.

Let us find now a non-Euclidean solution with Whitrow-Randall's relation. We refer to Berman and Gomide (1988) for the derivation of the following solution of the field equations, in the case $\ddot{\phi} = 0$. The reader can check that a solution is obtained for the above field equations (13.2.4) to (13.2.7) in the $k \neq 0$ case:

$$\rho = Ct^{-1}; \qquad (\ C = \text{constant}) \tag{13.2.18}$$

$$\phi = St; \qquad (\ S = \text{constant} \ ) \tag{13.2.19}$$

$$C = \frac{S(3+2\omega)}{8\pi}, \tag{13.2.20}$$

so that,

$$p = -\frac{S}{12\pi}(3+2\omega)t^{-1} = -\frac{2}{3}\rho \tag{13.2.21}$$

This equation of state was studied long ago by Whittaker (1966). At that time, negative pressures in a perfect gas law was an unusual property. However, when A. Guth published his inflationary solution, a negative pressure entered for explaining the inflationary scenario. Nowadays, with accelerating models for the present Universe, these equations of state are again revisited. Berman and Som (1990) also had pointed that negative pressures could play an important role in the formation of galaxies due to growing instabilities.

We can see from (13.2.5) that

$$\omega = \frac{6}{5}(1+kD^{-2}) \tag{13.2.22}$$

Though when we presented the above model, we had in mind non-Euclidean cases, we can not neglect also the following $k = 0$ solution, which has only an historical value, due to the small result for ω :

$$\omega = \tfrac{6}{5} \,, \tag{13.2.23}$$

and

$$m = 1. \tag{13.2.24}$$

We conclude that the constant deceleration parameter models of Berman, pick-up those cases in BD theory, that are exactly compatible with Whitrow-Randall's relation. Beesham (1995) has found other valid solutions for our problem.

13.3.   Mach's Principle and General Relativity

When we consider Einstein's field equations for the homogeneous isotropic Robertson-Walker's metric,

$$ds^2 = dt^2 - \frac{R(t)^2}{\left(1 + \frac{kr^2}{4}\right)^2} d\sigma^2 \,, \tag{13.3.1}$$

where,

$$d\sigma^2 = dx^2 + dy^2 + dz^2 \,. \tag{13.3.2}$$

For a perfect fluid, with the usual definition of the Hubble's parameter,

$$H = \frac{\dot{R}}{R} \,, \tag{13.3.3}$$

the field equations are,

$$\kappa\rho = 3H^2 + 3kR^{-2} + \Lambda, \tag{13.3.4}$$

and,

$$\kappa p = -2\ddot{R}R^{-1} - H^2 - kR^{-2} - \Lambda. \tag{13.3.5}$$

We recall the definition of the deceleration parameter,

$$q = -\frac{\ddot{R}R}{\dot{R}^2} \,. \tag{13.3.6}$$

By combining (13.3.4), (13.3.5), and (13.3.6), we obtain the following relation:

$$q = -\tfrac{4\pi}{3}\sigma H^{-2} = -\tfrac{4\pi}{3}\left(\rho + 3p - \tfrac{2\Lambda}{\kappa}\right)H^{-2} \,. \tag{13.3.7}$$

The above resembles Whitrow-Randall's relation, but it is exact.   Gomide and Berman(1988), have called it, the Whitrow-Randall's exact relation. We have, above, defined σ, which is called the gravitational mass parameter.

Consider a Universe where the Λ constant is "powerful": we will find,

$$\sigma \cong -\tfrac{2\Lambda}{\kappa}\,.$$
(13.3.8)

Now, we see that,

$$q \cong -\tfrac{\Lambda}{3}H^{-2}.$$
(13.3.9)

Present Universe observations, conform to the above hypothesis, (13.3.8), so that, for a positive lambda, we would have, as asserted, a negative deceleration parameter or, the Universe is accelerating.

From the exact derivation of Whitrow-Randall's relation for the Universe, we are led to induce that the Universe is Machian!!!

13.4.   Pryce-Hoyle Cosmology and Mach's Principle

Hoyle (1948) introduced, in Cosmology, an additional term towards the energy momentum tensor, originated by a scalar field, responsible for matter injection. This field, due to Pryce, Hoyle and Narlikar (Narlikar, 1993; Hoyle and Narlikar, 1963; Berman and Marinho Jr., 1996), is represented by:

$$T^{\mu\nu} = T_M^{\mu\nu} - f\left(\lambda^\mu\lambda^\nu - \tfrac{1}{2}g^{\mu\nu}\lambda^\alpha\lambda_\alpha\right),$$
(13.4.1)

where, $T_M^{\mu\nu}$ stands for the normal matter energy-momentum tensor, and F is a constant, while λ_μ is a vector given by:

$$\lambda_\mu = \tfrac{\partial\lambda}{\partial x^\mu} = \left(0,0,0,\dot{\lambda}\right).$$
(13.4.2)

This vector, represents essentially a negative energy density stemming from matter injection.

Einstein's equations are kept like:

$$G^{\mu\nu} = -\kappa T^{\mu\nu}$$
(13.4.3)

There is an additional relation,

$$n = j^\mu_{;\mu}\,,$$
(13.4.4)

which stands for the number of particles injected per unit of proper 4-volume, the particle current being represented by j^μ . For Robertson-Walker's metric,

$$ds^2 = dt^2 - \frac{R^2(t)}{\left[1+\left(\frac{kr^2}{4}\right)\right]^2}d\sigma^2 , \qquad (13.4.5)$$

where,

$$d\sigma^2 = dx^2 + dy^2 + dz^2 , \qquad (13.4.6)$$

we find the following field equations:

$$\kappa\rho = 3\left(\frac{\dot{R}}{R}\right)^2 + 3\frac{k}{R^2} + \tfrac{1}{2}\kappa f\dot{\lambda}^2 , \qquad (13.4.7)$$

and,

$$\kappa p = -2\frac{\ddot{R}}{R} - \left(\frac{\dot{R}}{R}\right)^2 - \frac{k}{R^2} + \tfrac{1}{2}\kappa f\dot{\lambda}^2 . \qquad (13.4.8$$

Additionally we have an equation for matter injection proper,

$$\ddot{\lambda} + 3\dot{\lambda}\frac{\dot{R}}{R} = f^{-1}n = f^{-1}j^\mu_{;\mu}. \qquad (13.4.9)$$

Consider now a flat Universe ($k = 0$). A solution with constant deceleration parameter, $q = 2$, can be found, featuring the scale factor,

$$R(t) = \sqrt[3]{3DT} \qquad (D = \text{constant}). \qquad (13.4.10)$$

The perfect fluid is found, with,

$$p = \alpha\rho = \alpha A t^{-2} , \qquad (13.4.11)$$

where ,

$$\alpha = \frac{1+S}{3+S}, \qquad (13.4.12)$$

and,

$$S = \tfrac{9}{2}C_1'^2 f\kappa = \text{constant} . \qquad (13.4.13)$$

The origin of the constants C_1' and A lies in the solution for λ , namely,

$$\lambda = C_1 \log t, \qquad (13.4.14)$$

while, we must obey the condition,

$$\kappa A = \tfrac{1}{3} + \tfrac{\kappa}{2}fC_1' . \qquad (13.4.15)$$

The pressure is found to be,

$$p = \left[\frac{1}{9\kappa} + \frac{fC_1'^2}{2}\right] t^{-2} . \tag{13.4.16}$$

Though this model is not a bit realistic, if we impose that the constant A be equal to $\frac{6}{\kappa}$, and, if,

$$fC_1' = \frac{34}{3\kappa} , \tag{13.4.17}$$

then, we find the "exact" Machian Whitrow-Randall relation (12.1.3).

We invite the reader to find other possible solutions for the above field equations.

For instance, let us work something not found by Berman and Marinho Jr. in their paper cited above: the inflationary flat Universe, with $\dot{\lambda} = $ constant.

From the field equations, with,

$$R = R_0 e^{Ht} . \qquad (R_0 = \text{constant}) \tag{13.4.18}$$

$$\ddot{\lambda} = 0 .$$

$$\dot{\lambda} = \frac{n}{3fH} = \text{constant.} \tag{13.4.19}$$

$$\kappa\rho = 3H^2 + \kappa\frac{f}{2}\dot{\lambda}^2 = 3H^2 + \frac{\kappa}{18f}H^{-2}n^2 = \text{constant.} \tag{13.4.20}$$

$$\kappa p = -3H^2 + \frac{\kappa}{18f}H^{-2}n^2 = \text{constant.} \tag{13.4.21}$$

It is supposed, in the above model, that n is constant!!! Whitrow-Randall's relation would also be applicable in this case...

13.5. Combined Einstein-Cartan-Brans-Dicke Machian Universe

Because we have dealt above, with the rotation of the Machian Universe, and this is about "spin", we would like examine a model involving intrinsic spin, like Einstein-Cartan's gravitational theory. Berman(2006g), examined the time behavior of shear and vorticity in a lambda-Universe, for inflationary models, in a Brans-Dicke framework. The resulting scenario is that exponential inflation smooths the fluid, in order to become a nearly perfect one after the inflationary period. We now examine the inclusion of spin, by means of Einstein-Cartan's theory, when a scalar field of Brans-Dicke origin, is included, along with a Cosmological lambda-term. Einstein-Cartan's gravitational theory, though not bringing vacuum solutions different than those in General Relativity theory, has an important rôle, by tying macrophysics, through gravitational and electromagnetic phenomena (i.e., involving constants G and c), with microphysics, though Planck's constant, involving spin originated by torsion. Spin is a subatomic integrant; it does not appear in macrophysics. This characteristic of Einstein-Cartan's gravitational theory, makes it a kind of bridge from Classical gravitational into Quantum theory.

Due to spin, Robertson-Walker's metric may not be representative of Physical reality in a torsioned spacetime. Nevertheless, we have shown in several papers (Berman, 1990f; 1991c), how anisotropic Bianchi-I models in Einstein-Cartan's theory could be reduced to Robertson-Walker's prototype, by defining overall, deceleration parameters, and scale-factors; we did the same thing, with other papers dealing with anisotropic models in GRT and BD theories [for GRT see (Berman, 1988; Berman and Som, 1989e); for BD theory see (Berman and Som, 1989)]. On the other hand, Berman and Som (2006) have shown that, slight deviations from Robertson-Walker's metric, changing it to a Bianchi-I metric, are enough to produce the anisotropic phenomena, like entropy production, or other ones; this is a clue to the possibility of considering overall scale-factors and deceleration parameters, etc, in the Raychaudhuri's equation for Einstein-Cartan's Cosmology, without worrying with any anisotropy, which becomes implicit in the equation as is shown by Raychaudhuri (1979). The essential modification of General Relativistic Bianchi-I cosmology, when we carry towards Einstein-Cartan's, resides, when field equations are explicited, in that the normal energy momentum tensor components T_1^1, T_2^2 and T_3^3 are subtracted by a term S^2, while T_0^0 is added by S^2. Of course, there appear also non-diagonal $S-$ dependent terms: for instance, T_3^2 and T_2^3 depend linearly with S^{32}. In our treatment of the Einstein-Cartan-Brans-Dicke theory, the field equations are obviously satisfied, but we have short-cutted the derivations, like we have done in the previous paper (Berman, 2006g), which also conforms with the field equations of that case (Brans-Dicke theory with lambda).

It is generally accepted that scalar tensor cosmologies play a central rôle in the present view of the very early Universe (Berman, 2007a). The cosmological "constant", which represents quintessence, is a time varying entity, whose origin remounts to Quantum theory(Berman, 2007). The first, and most important scalar tensor theory was devised by Brans and Dicke(1961), which is given in the "Jordan's frame". Afterwards, Dicke(1962) presented a new version of the theory, in the "Einstein's frame", where the field equations resembled Einstein's equations, but time, length, and inverse mass, were scaled by a factor $\phi^{-\frac{1}{2}}$ where ϕ stands for the scalar field. Then, the energy momentum tensor T_{ij} is augmented by a new term Λ_{ij}, so that:

$$G_{ij} = -8\pi G\,(T_{ij} + \Lambda_{ij}), \tag{13.5.1}$$

where G_{ij} stands for Einstein's tensor. The new energy tensor quantity, is given by:

$$\Lambda_{ij} = \tfrac{2\omega+3}{16\pi G\phi^2}\left[\phi_i\phi_j - \tfrac{1}{2}G_{ij}\phi_k\phi^k\right]. \tag{13.5.2}$$

In the above, ω is the coupling constant. The other equation is:

$$\Box \log\phi = \tfrac{8\pi G}{2\omega+3}T, \tag{13.5.3}$$

where $\Box$ is the generalized d'Alembertian, and $T = T_i^i$. It is useful to remember that the energy tensor masses are also scaled by $\phi^{-\frac{1}{2}}$.

For the Robertson-Walker's flat metric,

$$ds^2 = dt^2 - \frac{R^2(t)}{\left[1+\left(\frac{kr^2}{4}\right)\right]^2} d\sigma^2 \,, \tag{13.5.4}$$

where $k = 0$ and $d\sigma^2 = dx^2 + dy^2 + dz^2$.

The field equations, now read, in the alternative Brans-Dicke (Einstein's frame) reformulation (Raychaudhuri, 1979):

$$\frac{8\pi G}{3} \left(\rho + \frac{\Lambda}{\kappa} + \rho_\lambda\right) = H^2 \equiv \left(\frac{\dot{R}}{R}\right)^2 . \tag{13.5.5}$$

$$-8\pi G \left(p - \frac{\Lambda}{\kappa} + \rho_\lambda\right) = H^2 + \frac{2\ddot{R}}{R}. \tag{13.5.6}$$

In the above, we have:

$$\rho_\lambda = \frac{2\omega+3}{32\pi G} \left(\frac{\dot\phi}{\phi}\right)^2 = \rho_{\lambda 0} \left(\frac{\dot\phi}{\phi}\right)^2 . \tag{13.5.7}$$

From the above equations (13.5.5), (13.5.6) and (13.5.7) we obtain:

$$\frac{\ddot{R}}{R} = -\frac{4\pi G}{3} \left(\rho + 3p + 4\rho_\lambda - \frac{\Lambda}{4\pi G}\right) . \tag{13.5.8}$$

Relation (13.5.8) represents Raychaudhuri's equation for a perfect fluid. By the usual procedure, we would find the Raychaudhuri's equation in the general case, involving shear (σ_{ij}) and vorticity (ϖ_{ij}); the acceleration of the fluid is null for the present case, and then we find, along with Berman (Berman, 2006g):

$$3\dot{H} + 3H^2 = 2\left(\varpi^2 - \sigma^2\right) - 4\pi G(\rho + 3p + 4\rho_\lambda) + \Lambda \,, \tag{13.5.9}$$

where Λ stands for a cosmological "constant". As we are mimicking Einstein's field equations, Λ in (13.5.9) stands like it were a constant (see however, Berman, 2007, 2007a, 2006, 2006b). Notice that, when we impose that the fluid is not accelerating, this means that the quadri-velocity is tangent to the geodesics, i.e., the only interaction is gravitational.

When Raychaudhuri's equation is calculated for non-accelerated fluid, taken care of Einstein-Cartan's theory, combined with Brans-Dicke theory, the following equation was found by us, based on the original calculation for Einstein-Cartan's theory by Raychaudhuri (1979):

$$3\dot{H} + 3H^2 = 2\varpi^2 - 2\sigma^2 - 4\pi G(\rho + 3p + 4\rho_\lambda) + \Lambda + 128\pi^2 S^2 \,, \tag{13.5.10}$$

where S stands for the spin contents of the fluid, where we have omitted a term like

$$\varpi S = \varpi_{ik} S^{ik} + \varpi^{ik} S_{ik}, \tag{13.5.10a}$$

which is to be included in the pressure and energy density terms, by a re-scaling.

It is important to stress, that relation (13.5.10) is the same general relativistic equation, with the additional spin term, which transforms it into Einstein-Cartan's equation. When we work a combined Einstein-Cartan's and Brans-Dicke theory (BCDE theory), we would need to calculate the new field equations for the combined theory; a plausibility reasoning that substitutes an otherwise lengthy calculation, is the following: the term with spin, as well as it is added to the other general relativistic terms in equation (13.5.10), should be added equally to equation (13.5.9), because this is the Brans-Dicke equation in a general relativistic format. This equation is written in the unconventional format (Dicke, 1962), i.e., the alternative system of equations. We could not write so simply equation (13.5.10) if the terms in it were those of conventional Brans-Dicke theory.

Consider now exponential inflation, like we find in Einstein's theory:

$$R = R_0 e^{Ht},$$ (13.5.11)

and, as usual in General Relativity inflationary models,

$$\Lambda = 3H^2 .$$ (13.5.12)

For the time being, H is just a constant, defined by $H = \frac{\dot{R}}{R}$. We shall see, when we go back to conventional Brans-Dicke theory, that H is not the Hubble's constant.

From (13.5.11), we find $H = H_0 = $ constant.

A solution of Raychaudhuri's equation (13.5.10), would be the following:

$$\sigma = \sigma_0 e^{-\frac{\beta}{2}t} ;$$

$$\varpi = \varpi_0 e^{-\frac{\beta}{2}t} ;$$

$$\rho = \rho_0 e^{-\beta t} ;$$

$$p = p_0 e^{-\beta t} ;$$ (13.5.13)

$$\phi = \phi_0 e^{-\frac{\beta}{2}\sqrt{A}} e^{-\frac{\beta}{2}t} .$$

$$\Lambda = \Lambda_0 = \text{constant}.$$

In the above, σ_0 , ϕ_0 , p_0 , ρ_0 and β are constants, and

$$\beta = -4H.$$ (13.5.14)

The ultimate justification for this solution is that one finds a good solution in the conventional units theory, and, of course, that it obeys the field equations.

The spin of the Universe, S, has been identified (Berman, 2006b), with:

$$S = G^{-1}c^3 R^2 .$$

(13.5.15)

Without going into details on the origin of relation (13.5.15), it suffices to state that this is the Machian result (Berman, 2006b), and, anyway, it can be taken, as in (13.5.15), because it yields an acceptable solution, in agreement with the field equations.

When we return to conventional units, we retrieve the following corresponding solution:

$$\bar{R} = R_0 \phi^{\frac{1}{2}} e^{Ht} ;$$

$$\bar{\rho} = \rho_0 \phi^{-2} e^{-\beta t};$$

$$\bar{p} = p_0 \phi^{-2} e^{-\beta t} = \left[\frac{p_0}{\rho_0} \right] \bar{\rho} ;$$

(13.5.16)

$$\bar{\sigma} = \sigma \phi^{-\frac{1}{2}} ;$$

$$\bar{\varpi} = \varpi \phi^{-\frac{1}{2}} ;$$

$$\bar{\Lambda} = \Lambda_0 \phi^{-1};$$

$$\bar{\phi} = \phi = \phi_0 e^{-\frac{\beta}{2} \sqrt{A}\, e^{-\frac{\beta}{2} t}} .$$

$$\bar{S} = S = G^{-1} R^2 \quad , \text{ in } c = 1 \text{ units.}$$

As we promised to the reader, H is not the Hubble's constant. Instead, we find:

$$\bar{\Lambda} = \Lambda_0\, \phi_0^{-1}\, e^{\frac{\beta}{2} \sqrt{A}\, e^{-\frac{\beta}{2} t}} ;$$

(13.5.17)

$$\bar{\rho} = \rho_0\, \phi_0^{-2}\, e^{\beta \left[\sqrt{A}\, e^{-\frac{\beta}{2} t} - t \right]} ;$$

(13.5.18)

$$\bar{p} = p_0\, \phi_0^{-2}\, e^{\beta \left[\sqrt{A}\, e^{-\frac{\beta}{2} t} - t \right]} ;$$

(13.5.19)

$$\bar{R} = R_0\, \phi_0^{-\frac{1}{2}}\, e^{\left[Ht - \frac{1}{4}\beta \sqrt{A}\, e^{-\frac{\beta}{2} t} \right]} ;$$

(13.5.20)

$$\bar{\sigma} = \sigma_0\, \phi_0^{-\frac{1}{2}}\, e^{-\frac{1}{2}\beta \left[t - \frac{1}{2} \sqrt{A}\, e^{-\frac{\beta}{2} t} \right]} ,$$

(13.5.21)

$$\bar{\varpi} = \varpi_0\, \phi_0^{-\frac{1}{2}}\, e^{-\frac{1}{2}\beta \left[t - \frac{1}{2} \sqrt{A}\, e^{-\frac{\beta}{2} t} \right]} ,$$

(13.5.22)

$$\bar{S} = S = G^{-1} R_0^2 e^{2Ht} ,$$

(13.5.23)

and,

$$\overline{H} = H \, \phi_0^{-\frac{1}{2}} \, e^{\frac{1}{4}\beta\sqrt{A}} \, e^{-\frac{\beta}{2}t}. \tag{13.5.23 a}$$

From the hypothesis of an expanding Universe, we have to impose:

$$\overline{H} > 0. \tag{13.5.24}$$

Returning to Raychaudhuri's equation, we have the following condition to be obeyed by the constants:

$$\sigma_0^2 - \varpi_0^2 = -2\pi G \left[\rho_0 + 3p_0 + 4\rho_{\lambda0}\right] + 128\pi^2 G^{-2} R_0^4, \tag{13.5.25}$$

We now investigate the limit when $t \longrightarrow \infty$ of the above formulae, having in mind that, by checking that limit, we will know which ones increase or decrease with time; of course, we can not stand with an inflationary period unless it takes only an extremely small period of time. We shall suppose that $\beta = -4H < 0$.

We find:

$$\lim_{t \longrightarrow \infty} \overline{H} = 0;$$

$$\lim_{t \longrightarrow \infty} \overline{R} - \infty;$$

$$\lim_{t \longrightarrow \infty} \overline{\sigma} = \lim_{t \longrightarrow \infty} \overline{\varpi} = 0;$$

$$\lim_{t \longrightarrow \infty} \overline{\rho} = \lim_{t \longrightarrow \infty} \overline{p} = 0;$$

$$\lim_{t \longrightarrow \infty} \overline{\Lambda} = 0;$$

$$\lim_{t \longrightarrow \infty} \overline{\phi} = \infty.$$

As we can check, the scale factor, spin, and the scalar field, are time-increasing, while all other elements of the model, namely, vorticity, shear, Hubble's parameter, energy density, cosmic pressure, and cosmological term, as described by the above relations, decay with time. This being the case, shear is decaying, so that, after inflation, we retrieve a nearly perfect fluid, excepted the spin term: inflation has the peculiarity of removing shear, but not spin, from the model. It has to be remarked, that pressure and energy density obey a perfect gas equation of state. We do not worry with the increasing spin, because this only refers to the brief period of inflation; anyway, Berman (2007) has shown that the angular speed of the Universe varies with R^{-1} , so that, the growth of spin includes a shrinking of angular speed.

We have on purpose, left the solutions in terms of the negative constant β , in order that the reader might compare the above results, with the corresponding pure Brans-Dicke solution for the same problem, as in Berman(2006g). Of course, β is negative because the Universe is expanding, i.e., $H > 0$.

Part VI

NEW CENTURY DEVELOPMENTS AND CONCLUSIONS

Chapter 14

New Century Developments

14.1. Brief History of Black-Holes and the Universe

When a certain charged rotating body enters in gravitational collapse, a Kerr-Newman black-hole is formed(Newman et al., 1965). Only three parameters define this "hole": its mass M, charge Q, and rotational parameter "a", such that $a = -\frac{J}{M}$, where J is its total angular-momentum. The energy contents, within a "radial" distance ρ, of a Kerr-Newman b.h., may be found from the relation derived in Section 10.3.,

$$E = Mc^2 - \frac{GM^2}{4\rho}\left[1 + \left(\frac{a^2+\rho^2}{a\rho}\right)arctgh\left(\frac{a}{\rho}\right)\right] \tag{14.1.1}$$

where ρ is the positive root of:

$$\frac{x^2+y^2}{\rho^2+a^2} + \frac{z^2}{\rho^2} = 1 . \tag{14.1.2}$$

While collapse is in process, ρ will become smaller, up to the point when E becomes null, and, afterwards, negative. We have suggested that when $E \leq 0$, the negative energy contents E within a certain ρ value, is characteristic of repulsive gravitation, or antigravity.

In such case, the collapse will be deaccelerated, and eventually, halted at a non-null final radius, and then reversed towards a radially increasing direction: the outcome is a surging white-hole, originated from a non-null initial radius, which is also the mentioned end-point of gravitational collapse.

The endpoint of gravitational collapse may be, thus, *NOT* a black-hole with singular point of infinite energy density, but an expanding white-hole(Berman, 2004 a). The positivity of total energy, is still given by Mc^2, which is positive for ordinary matter. We can get a taste of involved energy densities in the halting point, by obtaining the energy inside a spherical non-rotating "ball", with $Q = a = 0$, where,

$$E = Mc^2 - \frac{GM^2}{2R} . \tag{14.1.3}$$

We obtain for the energy density μ :

$$\mu = \frac{dE}{dV} = \frac{1}{4\pi R^2} \frac{dE}{dR} = \frac{GM^2}{8\pi R^4} \ . \tag{14.1.4}$$

For $E = E_0 = 0$ we find:

$$R = R_0 = \frac{GM}{2c^2} \ , \tag{14.1.5}$$

while:

$$\mu = \mu_0 = \frac{2}{\pi} G^{-3} M^{-2} c^8 \ . \tag{14.1.6}$$

The mass density is obtained by dividing μ by c^2, so that, for the Sun,

$$\mu_{0Sun}/c^2 \approx 10^{21} \quad \text{g/cm}^3 \ .$$

The general result is, numerically, when M is given in grams,

$$\mu_0/c^2 \approx 10^{87} M^{-2} \quad \text{g/cm}^3 \ .$$

For the whole Universe, we estimate the very early mass as $\approx 10^{-5}$ grams, which is Planck's mass, so that the maximum big-crunch mass density would be $\approx 10^{97}$ g/cm^3 .

It is possible to view another scenario for collapse into black holes endpoint. We have shown that the Machian Universe obeys, in the very early phase, the equation of state:

$$p = -\frac{1}{3}\rho \ .$$

We have also seen that, in Einstein's General Relativity, the above equation of state carries the Planck's Universe into an exponential inflationary phase. Our model implies that $\Lambda \neq 0$. It can be shown that, in particular, Brans-Dicke Cosmology offers a similar scenario (Berman, 2006 h) . The interesting feature of the model presented earlier, is that the Universe is thought as a black hole, and that it begins with zero radius and zero mass, when we forget Quantum effects. Reversing the argument, we would be able to say that a black hole like the Universe, upon collapse, would end in a $M = 0$ and $R = 0$ state. Though our line of thought is entirely original, it matches what the famous Indian cosmologist Abhas Mitra has proposed since a long time ago (Mitra, 2006).

14.2. Conclusion

After the preliminary chapters, on the mathematical and physical details concerning GRT, we dealt with black holes, taking into account important features, from modern Physics like gravitomagnetism, repulsive gravity, and dilaton black holes. We examined superpotential black hole energy calculations, and Machian viewpoints on the Universe. We saw how relatively disjoint subjects, like zero-total energy Universes, and Pioneer's anomalous acceleration, may be closely related. Several extensions of GRT, like Brans-Dicke theory or Pryce-Hoyle Cosmology, are tied to Mach's Principle.

We suggest that the reader try to understand better, the nature of extra dimensional theories, in order to decide about important subjects, like the time-variation of fundamental "constants", though we have not treated these subjects here. Future research in modern Physics, shall be certainly necessary in order to decide about the contemporary problems of Physics, like the unification of gravitation with other interactions. It is not clear by now, whether such super-unified approach will be fruitfull in the next few years, nor whether such unification is in fact possible. Indeed, for some scientists, gravitational forces may not be ever treated along with the other three, within the same theoretical framework.

This author concludes with the following remark:

Physics is beautiful.

References and Suggested Bibliography

Abdel-Rahman,A.-M.M. (1992) - *Physical Review* **D45**, 3497.

Adler, R.J.; Bazin, M.; Schiffer, M. (1975) - *Introduction to General Relativity.* 2nd Edition. McGraw-Hill. New York.

Adler, R.J.; Silbergleit, A.S. (2000) - *International Journal of Theoretical Physics,* **39**, 1291.

Aguirregabiria, J.M. et al. (1996) - *Gen. Rel. and Grav.* **28**, 1393.

Albrecht, A.; Magueijo, J. (1998) - *A Time Varying Speed of Light as a Solution to Cosmological Puzzles,* preprint.

Arbab, A.I.(1997) - *GRG* **29**, 61.

Arbab, A.I.; Abdel-Rahman, A.-M.M. (1994) - *Physical Review D* **50**, 7725.

Augustine, Saint (1958) - *God's City*, (in Spanish), B.A.C., Madrid.

Barbour, J.; Pfister, H.; eds. (1995) - *Mach's Principle: From Newton's Bucket to Quantum Gravity*, Birkhäuser, Boston.

Barrow, J.D. (1983). in *The Very Early Universe.*, Gibbons, G.N., Hawking, S.W., and Siklos, S.T.C., eds., Cambridge University Press, Cambridge.

Barrow, J.D. (1987) *Phys. Rev.,* **D35**, 1805.

Barrow, J.D. (1990 a) *Phys Lett.B* **235**,40.

Barrow, J.D. (1990) - in *Modern Cosmology in Retrospect.* Edited by B.Bertotti, R. Balbinot, S.Bergia and A.Messina, Cambridge U.P., Cambridge.

Barrow, J.D. (1991) *Theories of Everything*, Oxford UP, Oxford.

Barrow, J.D. (1992) *Phys.Rev* **D46**, R3227.

Barrow, J.D. (1993) *Phys. Rev* **D47**, 5329.

Barrow, J.D. (1993 a) Phys.Rev. **D48**, 3592.

Barrow, J.D. (1994) *The Origin of the Universe*, Basic Books, NY.

Barrow, J.D. (1995) *Phys. Rev* **D51**, 2729.

Barrow, J.D. (1996) *MNRAS* **282**, 1397.

Barrow, J.D. (1997) *Varying G and Other Constants* , Los Alamos Archives http://arxiv.org/abs/gr-qc/9711084 v1 27/nov/1997.

Barrow, J.D. (1998) *Cosmologies with Varying Light Speed*, Los Alamos Archives http://arxiv.org/abs/Astro–Ph 9811022 v1.

Barrow, J.D. (2002) - *Los Alamos Archives* http://arxiv.org/abs/gr-qc/0211074

Barrow, J.D. (2002a) - *Los Alamos Archives* http://arxiv.org/abs/gr-qc/0209080

Barrow, J.D. (2004) - *Los Alamos Archives* http://arxiv.org/abs/gr-qc/0409062

Barrow, J.D. (2004a) - *Los Alamos Archives* http://arxiv.org/abs/gr-qc/0403084

Barrow, J.D. (2005) - *Los Alamos Archives* http://arxiv.org/abs/astro-ph/0503434

Barrow, J.D. ; et al (2003) - *Los Alamos Archives* http://arxiv.org/abs/astro-ph/0307227

Barrow, J.D. ; et al (2003a) - *Los Alamos Archives* http://arxiv.org/abs/gr-qc/0305075

Barrow, J.D. ; et al (2003b) - *Los Alamos Archives* http://arxiv.org/abs/astro-ph/0303014

Barrow, J.D. ; et al (2003c) - *Los Alamos Archives* http://arxiv.org/abs/gr-qc/0302094

Barrow, J.D. ; et al (2004) - *Los Alamos Archives* http://arxiv.org/abs/astro-ph/0406369

Barrow, J.D. ; Hervik, Sigbjorn (2002) - *Los Alamos Archives* http://arxiv.org/abs/gr-qc/0206061

Barrow, J.D. ; Hervik, Sigbjorn (2002a) - *Los Alamos Archives* http://arxiv.org/abs/gr-qc/0302076

Barrow, J.D. ; Hervik, Sigbjorn (2003) - *Los Alamos Archives* http://arxiv.org/abs/gr-qc/0304050

Barrow, J.D. ; Levin, Janna (2003) - *Los Alamos Archives* http://arxiv.org/abs/gr-qc/0304038

Barrow, J.D. ; Magueijo, J. (2005) - *Los Alamos Archives* http://arxiv.org/abs/astro-ph/0503222

Barrow, J.D. ; Mota, D. F. (2002) - *Los Alamos Archives* http://arxiv.org/abs/gr-qc/0207012

Barrow, J.D. ; Mota, D. F. (2002a) - *Los Alamos Archives* http://arxiv.org/abs/gr-qc/0212032

Barrow, J.D. ; Scherrer, Robert, J.(2004) - *Los Alamos Archives* http://arxiv.org/abs/astro-ph/0406088

Barrow, J.D. ; Shaw, Douglas, J. (2004a) - *Los Alamos Archives* http://arxiv.org/abs/gr-qc/0412135

Barrow, J.D. ; Subramanian, Kandaswamy (2002) - *Los Alamos Archives* http://arxiv.org/abs/astro-ph/0205312

Barrow, J.D. ; Tsagas, Christos, G.(2003) - *Los Alamos Archives* http://arxiv.org/abs/gr-qc/0309030

Barrow, J.D. ; Tsagas, Christos, G.(2003a) - *Los Alamos Archives* http://arxiv.org/abs/gr-qc/0308067

Barrow, J.D. ; Tsagas, Christos, G.(2004) - *Los Alamos Archives* http://arxiv.org/abs/gr-qc/0411070

Barrow, J.D. ; Tsagas, Christos, G.(2004a) - *Los Alamos Archives* http://arxiv.org/abs/gr-qc/0411045

Barrow, J.D.; Tipler, F.J. (1996) *The Anthropic Cosmological Principle* ,Oxford University Press, Oxford.

Barrow, J.D.;Carr, B.J. (1996) *Phys. Rev* **D54**, 3920.

Barrow, J.D.;Cotsakis S. (1988) *Physics Letters* **B214** 515.

Barrow, J.D.;Daborwski, M.P.(1995) – *MNRAS* **275**, 850.

Barrow, J.D.;Gotz, G. (1989) *Class.Quantum Gravity* **6**, 1253.

Barrow, J.D.;Liddle, A.R.(1993) *Phys. Rev* **D47**, R5219.

Barrow, J.D.;Maeda, K.(1990) *Nucl. Phys.* **B341**, 294.

Barrow, J.D.;Magueijo J.(1999)– *Solving the Flatness and Quasi Flatness Problems in Brans-Dicke Cosmologies with a Varying Light Speed* , Los Alamos Archives http://arxiv.org/abs/astro-ph/9901049 5/01/1999.

Barrow, J.D.;Mimoso, J.P.(1994) *Phys. Rev* **D50**, 3746.

Barrow, J.D.;Mimoso, J.P; Maia, M.R.G.(1993) *Phys. Rev* **D48**, 3630.

Barrow, J.D.;Saich, P.(1990) *Phys. Lett* **B249**, 406.

Beesham, A. (1986) - *International Journal of Theoretical Physics* **25**, 1295.

Beesham, A. (1993) - *Physical Review D* **48**, 3539.

Beesham, A. (1995) - *GRG* **27**, 15.

Bekenstein, J.D. (1974) - *Ann. Phys. (New York)* **82**, 535.

Bergmann,P.G. (1942) - *Introduction to the Theory of Relativity*, Prentice-Hall, reprinted by Dover, New York.

Bergmann,P.G. (1968) *Int.J.Theor.Phys.* **1**, 25.

Berman, M. S. (unpublished) M.Sc. thesis, Instituto Tecnológico de Aeronáutica, São José dos Campos, Brazil, (1981).

Berman,M.S. (1983) - *Nuovo Cimento* **74B**, 182.

Berman,M.S. (1988) - *GRG* **20**, 841.

Berman,M.S. (1988 b) - *GRG* **21**, 967.

Berman,M.S. (1989 b) - *Physics Letters A* **139**, 119.

Berman,M.S. (1989 d) - *Physics Letters A* **142**, 227.

Berman,M.S. (1989) - *Physics Letters A* **142**, 335.

Berman,M.S. (1990 a) - *International Journal of Theoretical Physics*, **29**, 567-570.

Berman,M.S. (1990 b) - *GRG* **22**,389.

Berman,M.S. (1990 c) - *International Journal of Theoretical Physics* **29**, 1415.

Berman,M.S. (1990 e) - *International Journal of Theoretical Physics* **29**, 571.

Berman,M.S. (1990 f) - *Nuovo Cimento B* **105**, 1373.

Berman,M.S. (1990 g) - *Nuovo Cimento B* **105**, 239.

Berman,M.S. (1990 h) - *Nuovo Cimento B* **105**, 235.

Berman,M.S. (1990 i) - *International Journal of Theoretical Physics* **29**, 1423.

Berman,M.S. (1990) - *International Journal of Theoretical Physics* **29**, 1419.

Berman,M.S. (1991 b) - *Physical Review D* **43**, 1075.

Berman,M.S. (1991 c) - *GRG* **23**, 1083.

Berman,M.S. (1991) - *GRG* **23**, 465.

Berman,M.S. (1992a) - *International Journal of Theoretical Physics* **31**, 1447.

Berman,M.S. (1992 b) - *International Journal of Theoretical Physics* **31**, 321.

Berman,M.S. (1992 c) - *International Journal of Theoretical Physics* **31**, 1217.

Berman,M.S. (1992 d) - *International Journal of Theoretical Physics* **31**, 329.

Berman,M.S. (1992 e) - *International Journal of Theoretical Physics* **31**, 1451.

Berman,M.S. (1992) - *International Journal of Theoretical Physics* **31**, 1217. This paper, by mistake was published in another Journal later (see Berman, 1994).

Berman,M.S. (1993) - *Learn How to Study Efficiently*, (In Portuguese), Ed. Albert Einstein, Curitiba.

Berman,M. S. (1994) - *Astrophys. Space Science,* **222**, 235.

Berman,M.S. (1994 a) - *International Journal of Theoretical Physics* **33**, 1929.

Berman,M.S. (1994) - *Astrophysics and Space Science* **215**, 135.

Berman,M.S. (1996 a) - *International Journal of Theoretical Physics* **35**, 1033.

Berman,M.S. (1996 b) - *International Journal of Theoretical Physics* **35**, 1719.

Berman,M.S. (1996) - *International Journal of Theoretical Physics* **35**, 1789.

Berman,M.S. (1997 a) - *International Journal of Theoretical Physics* **36**, 1461.

Berman,M.S. (1997) - *International Journal of Theoretical Physics* **36**, 1249.

Berman,M.S. (2004 a) - *Brief History of Black-Holes* - Los Alamos Archives http://arxiv.org/abs/gr-qc/0412054

Berman,M.S. (2004) - *Energy of Kerr-Newman Black-Holes and Gravitomagnetism - Los Alamos Archives* http://arxiv.org/abs/gr-qc/0407026

Berman,M.S. (2005) - *Misconceptions in Halliday,Resnick, and Walker's textbook - Los Alamos Archives* http://arxiv.org/abs/physics/0507110

Berman,M.S. (2006) - *Energy of Black-Holes and Hawking's Universe.* In *Trends in Black-Hole Research*, Chapter 5. Edited by Paul Kreitler, Nova Science, New York.

Berman,M.S. (2006b) - *Energy, Brief History of Black-Holes, and Hawking's Universe.* In *New Developments in Black-Hole Research*, Chapter 5. Edited by Paul Kreitler, Nova Science, New York.

Berman,M.S (2006c) - *On the Machian Properties of the Universe*, submitted to publication. *Los Alamos Archives*: http://www.arxiv.org/abs/physics/0610003

Berman, M.S. (2006d) - *On the Magnetic Field and Entropy Increase of a Machian Universe* - submitted to publication. *Los Alamos Archives* http://arxiv.org/abs/physics/0611007.

Berman, M.S. (2006e) - *The Pioneer anomaly and a Machian Universe* - submitted to publication. *Los Alamos Archives* http://arxiv.org/abs/physics/0606117.

Berman,M.S. (2006f) - *On a time variation of neutrino's mass* - Los Alamos Archives http://arxiv.org/abs/physics/0606208. Submitted.

Berman,M.S. (2006g) - *Shear and Vorticity in Inflationary Brans-Dicke Cosmology with Lambda-Term* - Los Alamos Archives http://arxiv.org/abs/physics/0703244 - to appear in *Astrophysics and Space Science.*

Berman,M.S. (2006 h) - *Cosmological Model for the Very Early Universe in B.D. Theory - Los Alamos Archives* http://arxiv.org/abs/gr-qc/0605092 - submitted.

Berman, M.S. (2006i) - *Combined Einstein-Cartan-Brans-Dicke Machian Universe - Los Alamos Archives* http://arxiv.org/abs/physics/0607005

Berman, M.S. (2006j) - *Gravitomagnetism and Angular Momenta of Black-Holes - Los Alamos Archives* http://arxiv.org/abs/physics/0608053 - *Revista Mexicana the Astronomia y Astrofísica*, **43**, 2 (2007).

Berman,M.S. (2006k) - *On the energy of the Universe* - Los Alamos Archives http://arxiv.org/abs/gr-qc/0605063v2.

Berman, M.S. (2006l) - *On the Machian Origin of Inertia* - Los Alamos Archives http://arxiv.org/abs/physics/0609026

Berman, M.S. (2006m) - *Is the Universe a White-hole?* - Los Alamos Archives http://arxiv.org/abs/physics/0612007 , to appear in *Astrophysics and Space Science.*

Berman,M.S. (2007) - *Introduction to General Relativity and the Cosmological Constant Problem.* Nova Science, New York.

Berman,M.S. (2007a) - *Introduction to General Relativistic and Scalar Tensor Cosmologies*, Nova Science, New York.

Berman, M.S.; Gomide, F.M. (1987) - *Tensor Calculus and General Relativity: an introduction.* (in Portuguese) - 2nd. ed., McGraw-Hill, São Paulo. [1st. edition in 1986].

Berman, M.S.; Marinho Jr., R. M. (1996) - Letter to the Editor, Physics Today, **49**, 13.

Berman, M.S.; Marinho Jr., R. M. (1996 b) - *Nuovo Cimento B,* **111**, 1279.

Berman, M.S.; Marinho Jr., R. M. (2001) - *Astroph. Space Science* **278**, 367.

Berman, M.S.; Paim, T. (1990) - *Nuovo Cimento B, **105**, 1377.*

Berman, M.S.; Som, M.M. (1993) - *Astrophysics and Space Science, **207**,* 105.

Berman, M.S.; Trevisan, L.A. (2001) - *On the Creation of the Universe out of Nothing - Los Alamos Archives* http://arxiv.org/abs/gr-qc/0104060

Berman,M.S.; Trevisan, L.A. (2001 b) - *On a time varying fine structure constant - Los Alamos Archives* http://arxiv.org/abs/gr-qc/0111102

Berman,M.S.; Trevisan, L.A. (2001 c) - *Estimate on the deceleration parameter in a Universe with variable fine structure constant* - Los Alamos Archives http://arxiv.org/abs/gr-qc/0111101

Berman,M.S.; Trevisan, L.A. (2001 d) - *Inflationary phase in Generalized Brans-Dicke theory - Los Alamos Archives* http://arxiv.org/abs/gr-qc/0111098

Berman,M.S.; Trevisan, L.A. (2001 e) - *Static Generalized Brans-Dicke Universe and Gravitational Waves Amplification - Los Alamos Archives* http://arxiv.org/abs/gr-qc/0111099

Berman,M.S.; Trevisan, L.A. (2001 f) - *Amplification of Gravitational Waves During Inflation in Brans-Dicke Theory - Los Alamos Archives* http://arxiv.org/abs/gr-qc/0111100

Berman,M.S.; Trevisan, L.A. (2001) - *Possible Cosmological Implications of Time Varying Fine Structure Constant - Los Alamos Archives* http://arxiv.org/abs/gr-qc/0112011

Berman,M.S.; Trevisan, L.A. (2002) - *Inflationary Phase with Time Varying Fundamental Constants - Los Alamos Archives* http://arxiv.org/abs/gr-qc/0207051

Berman,M.S.;Som, M.M. (1989 a) - *Physics Letters A* **142**, 338.

Berman,M.S.;Som, M.M. (1989 b) - *Progress Theor.Phys,* **81**, 823.

Berman,M.S.;Som, M.M. (1989 c) - *Phys. Letters A* **136**, 206.

Berman,M.S.;Som, M.M. (1989 d) - *Physics Letters A* **139**, 119.

Berman,M.S.;Som, M.M. (1989 e) - *GRG* , **21**, 967-970.

Berman,M.S.;Som, M.M. (1989 f) - *Physics Letters A* **136**, 428.

Berman,M.S.;Som, M.M. (1989)- *Nuovo Cimento* **103B**,N.2, 203.

Berman,M.S.;Som, M.M. (1990 b) - *International Journal of Theoretical Physics* **29**, 1411.

Berman,M.S.;Som, M.M. (1990) - *GRG* **22**, 625.

Berman,M.S.;Som, M.M. (1992) - *International Journal of Theoretical Physics* **31**, 325.

Berman,M.S.;Som, M.M. (1993 b) - *Journal of Mathematical Physics,* **34(1)**, 111 .

Berman,M.S.;Som, M.M. (1993) - *Astrophysics and Space Science*, **207**, 105.

Berman,M.S.;Som, M.M. (1995) - *Astrophys. Space.Sci*, **225**, 237.

Berman,M.S.;Som, M.M. (2007) - *Natural Entropy Production in an Inflationary Model for a Polarized Vacuum - Los Alamos Archives*: http://www.arxiv.org/abs/physics/0701070 - to appear in *Astrophysics and Space Science.*

Berman,M.S; Gomide, F.M. (1988) - *GRG* **20**, 191.

Berman,M.S; Gomide, F.M. (1994) - *International Journal of Theoretical Physics* **33**, 1931.

Berman,M.S; Gomide, F.M. (2006) - *On a time variation of Neutrinos' mass* - (submitted). *Los Alamos Archives*: http://www.arxiv.org/abs/physics/0606208.

Berman,M.S; Som, M.M.; Gomide, F.M. (1989) - *GRG* **21**, 287.

Bernardis, P. et al. (2000), *Nature* **404**, 955;

Bertolami, O. (1986 b). *Fortschritte der Physik,* **34**, (12), 829.

Bertolami, O.(1986) - *Nuovo Cimento B* **93**, 36.

Bondi, H.; Gold, T. (1948). *MNRAS*, **108**, 252.

Bonnor, W.; Cooperstock, F.I. (1989) - *Phys. Lett. A* **139**, 442.

Born, M. (1934) - *Proceedings Royal Society,* **143A**, 410.

Born, M. (1937) - *Ann. Inst. H. Poincaré.* **7**, 155.

Born, M.; Infeld, L. (1934) - *Proceedings Royal Society*, **144A**, 425.

Boyer, R.H.; Lindquist, R.W. (1967) - *Journal of Mathematical Physics,* **8**, 265.

Brans, C. (1962) - *Physical Review,* **125**, 2194.

Brans, C.; Dicke, R. H. (1961) - *Phys. Review* **124**, 925.

Brown, J.D.; Teitelboim, C.(1987) - *Physics Letters B* **195**, 177.

Burd A.B., Barrow J.D. (1988) *Nucl. Physics,* **B308**, 929.

Carmeli, M. (1982) - *Classical Fields* - Wiley, N.Y.

Carroll, S. M. (2001), *Living Rev. Rel.* **4**, 1.

Carvalho, J.C.; Lima, J.A.S. ;Waga, I. (1992) - *Physical Review D* **46**, 2404.

CERN-PH-TH (2004) - 142 - Masiero,A.; Vempati,S.K.; Vives,O. (2004) - *Massive Neutrinos and Flavour Violation*, CERN-PH-TH/2004-142.

Chaliassos, E. (1987). *Physica*, **144A**, 390.

Chamorro, A.; Virbhadra, K.S. (1996) - International Journal Modern Physics, **D5**, 251.

Chandrasekhar, S. (1983) - *The Mathematical Theory of Black Holes*, Oxford University Press, Oxford.

Chen,W.;Wu,Y.- S. (1990) - *Phys. Review D* **41**,695.

Chiu, H.-Y.; Hoffmann, W.F. eds (1964) - *Gravitation and Relativity,* Benjamin, New York.

Ciufolini, I. (2005) - *Los Alamos Archives* http://arxiv.org/abs/gr-qc/0412001 v3

Ciufolini, I.; Pavlis, E. (2004) - *Letters to Nature,* **431**, 958.

Ciufolini, I.; Wheeler, J. A. (1995) - *Gravitation and Inertia,* Princeton Univ. Press, Princeton. See especially page 82, # 72 to 83.

Collins, P.D.B.; Martin, A.D.; Squires, E.J. (1989) - *Particle Physics and Cosmology,* Wiley, New York.

Cooperstock, F.I.(1994) - *GRG* **26**, 323, .

Cooperstock, F.I.; Rosen, N. (1989) - *International Journal of Theoretical Physics,* **28**, 423 - 440.

Cooperstock, F.I.; Tieu, S. (2005) - submitted to Astrophysical Journal. See also *Los Alamos Archives* http://arxiv.org/abs/astro-ph/0507619.

Cooperstock,F.I.;Israelit,M. (1995) - *Foundations of Physics,* **25**, 631.

Cusa, N. (1954) - *Of Learned Ignorance ,* Routledge and Kegan Paul, London.

Dicke, R.H. (1959) - *Science* **129**, 621.

Dicke, R.H. (1962). *Physical Review,* **125**, 2163.

Dicke, R.H. (1964) - *The many faces of Mach,* in *Gravitation and Relativity,* W.A.Benjamin Inc. New York.

Dicke, R.H. (1964 a) - *The significance for the solar system of time-varying gravitation,* in *Gravitation and Relativity,* W.A.Benjamin Inc. New York.

Dicke, R.H. (1967) - *Physics Today* **20**, 55.

Dicke, R.H. et al. (1965) - *Ap. J.* **142**, 414.

D'Inverno, R. (1992) - *Introducing Einstein's Relativity.* Clarendon Press, Oxford.

Dirac, P.A.M. (1938) - *Proceedings of the Royal Society* **165 A**, 199.

Dirac, P.A.M. (1975) - *General Relativity ,* Wiley , New York.

Einstein, A. (1923) - *The Foundation of the General Theory of Relativity ,* in *Principle of Relativity ,* reprint by Dover, New York.; *Cosmological Considerations on the General Theory of Relativity,* idem.

Falco, E. E., Kochanek, C. S., Muñoz, J. A. (1998), *Astrophys. J.* **494**, 47.

Fardon, R.; Nelson A.E.; Weiner, N. (2003) - *Los Alamos Archives* http://arxiv.org/abs/astro-ph/0309800 v2.

"Fermilab" (2000) - *News Media Contact. Fermilab,* 00-12, July 20, 2000.

Feynman, R.P. - *Lectures on Gravitation ,* Addison-Wesley, Reading, (1962-3).

Franklin, A. (2000) - The Road to the Neutrino, *Physics Today,* **53**, N. 2, 22.

Freud, P.H. (1939)- *Ann. Math,* **40**, 417.

Garfinkle, D.; Horowitz, G.T.; Strominger, A. (1991) - Physical Review, **D43**, 3140.

Garfinkle, D.; Horowitz, G.T.; Strominger, A. (1992) - Physical Review, **D45**, 3888.

Goldstein, H. (1980) - *Classical Mechanics*, 2nd. Edition, Addison Wesley, Reading.

Gomide, F.M. (1956) - *An. Ac. Bras. Ci.* **23**, 179.

Gomide, F. M. (1963) - *Nuovo Cimento,* **30**, 672.

Gomide, F.M. (1965) - *An. Ac. Bras. Ci.* **37**, 425.

Gomide, F.M. (1966) - *Nuovo Cimento* **41**, 156.

Gomide, F.M. (1967) - *An. Ac. Bras. Ci.* **39**, 405.

Gomide, F.M. (1972) - *Nuovo Cimento* **12 B**, 11.

Gomide, F.M. (1973) - *Rev. Bras. Fis.* **3**, 3.

Gomide, F.M. (1976) - *Lett. Nuovo Cimento* **15**, 515.

Gomide, F.M. (1980) - *Lett. Nuovo Cimento* **29**, 399.

Gomide, F.M. (1985) - *Rev. Bras. Fis.* **15**,388.

Gomide, F.M.;Berman, M.S. (1988) - *Introduction to Relativistic Cosmology.* (in Portuguese) - 2nd ed., McGraw-Hill, São Paulo. [1st edition, 1986].

Gomide, F.M.;Berman, M.S.;Garcia, R.L. (1986) - *Rev. Mexicana Astron. Astrofis.* **12**, 46.

Gomide, F.M.;Uehara, M. (1975) - *Prog. Theoretical Physics* **53**, 1365.

Gomide, F.M.;Uehara, M. (1977) - *Rev. Bras. Fis.* **7**, 429.

Gomide, F.M.;Uehara, M. (1978) - *Rev. Bras. Fis.* **8**, 376.

Gomide, F.M.;Uehara, M. (1981) - *Astronomy and Astrophysics* **95**, 362.

Gomide, F.M.;Uehara, M. (1985) - *Ciência e Cultura* **37**, 83.

Gomide, F.M.;Uehara, M. (1985a) - *Rev. Bras. Fis.* **15**, 388.

Grischuk, L.P (1975 b)–*Lett. Nuovo Cimento* **12**, (2) 60.

Grischuk, L.P (1975)– *Sov.Phys. JETP* **40**,409.

Grischuk, L.P (1977)– *Ann. N.Y Acad. Sci* **302**, 439.

Grøn, Ø. (1986). *American Journal of Physics,* **54**, 46.

Gruber, R.P.; Price, R.H.; Matthews, S.M.; Cordwell, W.R.; Wagner, L.F. (1988) - *American Journal of Physics* **56**, 265.

Guth, A. (1981) - *Physical Review D* **23**, 347.

Halliday, D., Resnick, R., and Walker, J. (2005) *Fundamentals of Physics.* 7th. Edition. Wiley, New York. p. 339. Formula (13-21).

Halverson, N. W. et al. (2002), *Astrophys. J.*, **571**, 604.

Hawking, S.W. (1984) - *Physics Letters B* **134**, 403.

Hawking, S.W. (1993) - *Black Holes and Baby Universes and Other Essays* , Bantam Books, London.

Hawking, S.W. (1993 a) - *Hawking on the Big-Bang and Black Holes* , World Scientific, Singapore.

Hawking, S.W.(1975) - *Communications of Mathematical Physics* **43**, 199.

Hawking, S.W.(1988)(1996) *The Illustrated A Brief History of Time*, Bantam Books, New York.

Hawking, S.W.(2001) - "The Universe in a Nutshell", Bantam, New York.

Horvat, R. (2005) - *Los Alamos Archives* http://arxiv.org/abs/astro-ph/0505507 v2.

Hoyle, F. (1948). *MNRAS,* **108**, 372.

Hoyle, F.; Narlikar, J.V. (1963). *Proc. Royal Society,* **273A**, 1.

Kaplan, D.B. (2004) - *Physical Review Letters* **93**, 091801.

Katz, J. (1985) - *Classical and Quantum Gravity* **2**, 423.

Katz, J. (2006) - Private communication.

Katz, J.; Bičak, J.; Lynden-Bell, D. (1997) - *Physical Review* **D55**, 5957.

Katz, J.; Ori, A. (1990) - *Classical and Quantum Gravity* **7**, 787.

Kenyon, I.R. (1990) - *General Relativity.* Oxford U.P., Oxford.

Kerr, R. P. (1963) - *Physical Review Letters,* **11**, 237.

Kolb, E. W.; Turner, M. S. (1990) - *The Early Universe*, Addison Wesley, Redwood City.

Koyré, A. (1962) - *Du Mode Clos à L'Univers Infini*, Presses Universitaires de France.

Kramer, D.; Stephani, H.; MacCallum, M.; Heret, E. (1980). *Exact Solutions of Einstein's field equations.* Cambridge U.P., Cambridge.

Kreitler, P.V. (ed., 2006) - *Focus on Black Hole Research,* Nova Science, New York.

Kreitler, P.V. (ed., 2006a) - *New Developments in Black Hole Research,* Nova Science, New York.

Kreitler, P.V. (ed., 2006b) - *Trends in Black Hole Research,* Nova Science, New York.

La,D; Steinhardt,P.J (1989) – *Phys. Rev. Lett* **62**, 376.

Landau, L.; Lifshitz, E. - *The Classical Theory of Fields*, 4th. Revised ed.; Pergamon, Oxford, (1975).

Landsberg, P.T. (1983) - Private Communication.

Lederman, L. (1989) - Observations of Particle Physics from Two Neutrinos to the Standard Model, *Science*, **224**, 664 .

Levinson, A. (2006) - Chapter 4, in *Trends in Black Hole Research*, edited by P. V. Kreitler, Nova Science, New York.

Lightman, A.P.; Press, W.H.; Price, R.H.; Teukolsky, S.A. (1974) - *Problem Book in Relativity and Gravitation*, Princeton University Press, Princeton.

Linde, A.D. (1988) - *Physics Letters B* **200**, 272.

Linde, A. (1990). *Particle Physics and Inflationary Cosmology*. Harwood Acad. Press, N.Y.

Lovelock, D. and Rund, H. (1975) - *Tensors, Differential Forms, and Variational Principles*, Wiley, New York; reprinted with corrections, Dover, 1989, New York.

Lynden-Bell,D.;Katz, J. (1985) - *M.N.R.A.S.* **213**,21.

Mach, E. (1912) - *Die Mechanik in Ihrer ...* Brockhaus, Leipzig.

Mie, G. (1912) - *Ann. d. Phys.* **37**, 511.

Mie, G. (1912a) - *Ann. d. Phys.* **39**, 1.

Mie, G. (1913) - *Ann. d. Phys.* **40**, 1.

Misncr, C.W. ct al (1973) - see MTW below.

Misner, C.W.; Thorne, K.S.; Wheeler, J.A. (1973) *Gravitation* , Freeman, San Francisco.

Mitra, A. (2006) - Chapter 1 in *Focus on Black Hole Research*. Ed. by Paul V. Kreitler, Nova Science, New York.

Narlikar, J.V. (1993) - *Introduction to Cosmology*, 2nd. edition, Cambridge University Press, Cambridge. [First edition, Jones and Bartlett, 1983. I like the first edition best].

Newman, E. T.; Couch, E.; Chinnapared, R.; Exton, A.; Prakash, A.; Torence, R. (1965) - *Journal of Mathematical Physics* **6**, 918.

Nordtvedt, K. (1970) *Astrophys. J,* **161**, 1059.

North, J.D. (1965) - *The Measure of the Universe - A History of Modern Cosmology*, Clarendon Press, Oxford.

Novello, M. (1980). *Cosmologia Relativista* in II Escola de Cosmologia e Gravitação, ed by M.Novello, CBPF, Rio de Janeiro.

Ohanian, H. (1985) - *Physics*, Norton, New York.

O'Hanlon, J.; Tupper, B.O.J. (1972). *Nuovo Cimento*, **7B**, 305.

Overduin, J.M.; Cooperstock, F.I. (1998) - *Physical Review D* **58**, 043506.

Ozer,M;Taha,M. O .(1986) - *Phys. Lett. B* **171**,363.

Ozer,M.;Taha,M. O. (1987) - *Nucl. Phys.B* **287**,776.

Papapetrou, A.(1974) - *Lectures on General Relativity.* D. Reidel Publishing Company, Boston.

Pathria, R.K. (1972) - *Nature* **240**, 298.

Peccei, R.D; Solà, J.; and Wetterich, C. (1987) - *Physics Letters B* **195**, 183.

Peebles, P.J.E.; Ratra, B. (1988) - *Astrophysical Journal Lett. Ed.* **325**, L17.

Penrose, R. (2004) - *The Road to Reality*, Jonathan Cape, London.

Peratt, A.L. (1990) - *The Sciences, N.Y. Academy of Sciences*, No. **1**, 24.

"Physics Today" (2004) - Neutrino Oscillation Has Now Been Seen... , *Physics Today,* **57**, N. 7, 11.

Rabinowitz, M (2006) - in *Trends in Black Hole Research* , edited by P.V.Kreitler, Nova Science Publishers, New York.

Raine, D.; Thomas, E. (2005) - *Black Holes - An Introduction*, Imperial College Press, London.

Raychaudhuri, A.K (1979) - *Theoretical Cosmology*, Clarandon Press, Oxford.

Raychaudhuri, A.K. (1975) - *Physical Review.* **53**, 1360.

Raychaudhuri, A.K.; Banerji, S.; Banerjee, A. (1992). *General Relativity, Astrophysics, and Cosmology*, Springer-Verlag, New York.

Reissner, H. (1916) - *Ann. Phys.* **50**, 106.

Riess, A. G. et al. (1998), *Astron. J.* **116**, 1009.

Rosen, N. (1994) - *Gen. Rel. and Grav.* **26**, 319.

Rosen, N. (1995) - *GRG* **27**, 313.

Rowan-Robinson, M. (1981) - *Cosmology*, second edition. Oxford University Press, Oxford. (see page 72)

Sabbata, V.de; Gasperini, M. (1979) - *Lettere al Nuovo Cimento* **25**, 489.

Sabbata, V.de; Sivaram, C. (1994) - *Spin and Torsion in Gravitation*, World Scientific, Singapore.

Sahni,V.;Starobinski,A. (2000)-*Intl. J.Mod. Phys.* **D9**, 373. Also http://arXiv.org (:astro-ph/9904398 v2).

Schwarzschild, B. (1992) - *Physics Today,* **45**, N. 8, 17 .

Schwarzschild, B. (1998). *Physics Today,* **51** N.8.

Schwarzschild, B. (2001). *Physics Today,* **54** (7), 16.

Schwarzschild, B.(1998) - *Physics Today,* **51**, N. 8 .

Schwarzschild, K. (1916) - *Stizber. Deut. Akad. Wiss.*, Berlin, K1. *Math.-Phys. Tech.,* s. 189.

Schweber, S. (2002) - Enrico Fermi and Quantum Electrodynamics, *Physics Today,* **55**, N. 6,31.

Sciama, D.N. (1953). *MNRAS*, **113**, 34.

"Science" (1992) - Are Neutrinos' Mass Hunters Pursuing a Chimera?, *Science*, **256**, 731.

"Science" (1992a) - New Results Yeld no Culprit for Missing Neutrinos, *Science*, **256**, 1512.

"Science" (1999) - Search for Neutrino Mass... , *Science*, **283**, 928.

Sears,F.W.; Salinger, G.L. (1975) - *Thermodynamics, Kinetic Theory, and Statistical Thermodynamics*, Addison-Wesley, New York.

Sexl, R.; Sexl, H. (1979) - *White Dwarfs-Black Holes: An Introduction to Relativistic Astrophysics*, Academic Press, New York.

Shabad, A. E.; Usov, V.V. (2006) - *Physical Review Lett.* **96**, 180401.

Stephani, H. (1990) - *General Relativity,* 2nd ed., Cambridge Universtity Press, Cambridge.

Synge, J.L. (1960) - *Relativity: The General Theory*, North Holland, Amsterdam.

Taylor, E.F.; Wheeler, J.A. (2000) - *Exploring Black Holes - Introduction to General Relativity*, Addison Wesley Longman, San Francisco.

Taylor, J.H. ; Weisberg, J.M. (1982) - *Astrophysics Journal,* **253**, 908.

Taylor, J.H. ; Weisberg, J.M. (1989) - *Astrophysics Journal,* **345**, 434.

Thirring, H.; Lense, J. (1918) - *Phys. Z.* **19**, 156.

Tolman, R.C.(1934) - *Relativity, Thermodynamics and Cosmology , OUP.* Re-printed by Dover, New York (1987).

Virbhadra, K.S. (1990) - *Phys. Rev.* **D41**, 1086.

Virbhadra, K.S. (1990a) - *Phys. Rev.* **D42**, 2919.

Virbhadra, K.S. (1990b) - *Phys. Rev.* **D42**, 1066.

Waga, I. (1993) - *Ap. J.* **414**, 436.

Wagoner, R.V. (1970)- *Phys. Rev.* **D1** , 3209.

Weinberg, S. (1972) - *Gravitation and Cosmology*, Wiley, New York.

Weinberg, S. (1989) - *Reviews of Modern Physics*, **61**, 1.

Wesson, P.S. (1999) - *Space-Time-Matter (Modern Kaluza, Klein Theory)* , World Scientific, Singapore.

Wesson, P.S. (2006) - *Five Dimensional Physics*, World Scientific, Singapore.

Weyl, H. (1950) - *Space-time-matter*, Dover, N.Y.

Winterberg, F. (2002) - *The Planck Aether Hypothesis*, Gauss Scie. Press, N.V.

Wheeler, J.A. (1964) - *Mach's principle as boundary condition for Einstein's equations,* in Chiu and Hoffmann (1964).

Whitrow, G. (1946) - *Nature* **158**,165.

Whitrow, G.; Randall, D. (1951)-*MNRAS* **111**,455.

Whittacker, E.(1935) - *Proc. Royal Society* **149 A**, 384.

Whittacker, J.M. (1966) - *Nature.* **209**, 491.

Will, C.M. (1984) *Phys. Rep* **113**, 345.

Wrede, R.C.; Spiegel, M. (2002) - *Advanced Calculus*, Second Edition, McGraw-Hill, New York.

York Jr, J.W. (1980) - *Energy and Momentum of the Gravitational Field*, in *A Festschrift for Abraham Taub*, ed. by F.J. Tipler, Academic Press, N.Y.

Zel'dovich, Ya. B. (1967) *Pi'sma JETP .***6**, 887.

Zel'dovich, Ya. B. (1967 b) *JETP Lett.* **6**, 316.

Zel'dovich, Ya. B.(1968) - *Soviet Physics Usp.* **11**, 381.

Zel'dovich, Ya. B. (1981) *Sov. Phys. Usp.* **24**, 216.

INDEX